Laughter Is 𝓎

Laughter Is Your Lifeline

Jo-Dee Walmsley

FUZZY
FLAMINGO

Published by Fuzzy Flamingo
www.fuzzyflamingo.co.uk

ISBN 978-1-8380944-8-5

Cover design and Typesetting: Jen Parker, Fuzzy Flamingo
www.fuzzyflamingo.co.uk

I dedicate this book to Enriqué and Fatimeh, my beautiful kids.
You keep me striving to do the best that I can and to keep going,
even when I feel I can't. You are my lights at the end of the tunnel.
Love you always xx

Contents

Appendices

Foreword

Goodness me Jo-Dee, thank you so much for writing an engaging, helpful book whilst coming from a place of such knowing. Your journey had me quite breathless at times.

I first met Jo-Dee at a Professional Speaking Association event just a few short years ago and I had no idea the level of challenges she had faced and continues to face. She was and is always so upbeat, warm, kind and, of course, twinkling with laughter. A person who seriously walks her talk and eminently qualified to write this book.

It is not only full of tips and techniques that can be applied across all walks of life, it also takes the reader through a roller-coaster of personal hardships and triumphs that make us reflect on our own lives and how we can apply her teachings. All supported with a strong and relevant level of research.

The timing of publication is perfect in this troubled, uncertain world and I am utterly delighted that Jo-Dee has offered such a constructive tool to help get us through.

A book I thoroughly enjoyed reading and the notes I made will most certainly be put into action.

Thank you.

Dr Lynda Shaw
Neuroscientist and Author of *Your Brain Is Boss*

Chapter 1

Introduction – July 2020

A well-balanced person is one who finds both sides of an issue laughable

Herbert Procknow

How did I get here?

There is blood everywhere, it looks like I've been attacked by a rabid animal but, alas, it was just the doctor trying to find a vein that would take the cannula.

After lots of fist and teeth clenching, she finally did it. This is something I have become so used to by now; it seems I have 'designer veins' forming convoluted patterns with hardly any straight lines long enough to insert a cannula.

"You are going to ruin my reputation," says the doctor, as she cleans up the mess I had made all over the pillow.

"Yes, I do like to be a bit of a challenge," I laugh.

The nurses were doing my blood tests and giving me my antibiotics while chatting to me and Graham, my good friend and chaperone; more about him later…

As we were all speaking, Graham started answering with a song, and we were in stitches of laughter within minutes. Soon more nurses came to see what was going on.

As our comedy skit came to an end, I was being carted out of the Renal Daycare room in my rather large bed. It kept hitting the doors and banging into things. This made me laugh even more, especially when the hospital porter explained that the architects never think about the size of the existing beds when designing extensions to the hospital wings.

We weaved in and out of the corridors of the hospital for ages before eventually reaching the operating x-ray room. It was freezing, even with the blankets on, although I'm not sure if it was really the temperature; maybe I was a tad nervous.

I was lucky to have Graham by my side, making sure I was distracted by his really corny jokes. It certainly worked and I was grateful, having been up for a few nights feeling anxious about this 'lifeline' that was about to be inserted into my belly.

For some reason, I wasn't sure whether I was going to make it. There were thoughts of what complications there might be and, of course, what my future would look like once I needed to be attached to a machine.

Another thought floating around in my mind was whether I should make a video for my kids to tell them how much I loved them. I was about to have a catheter (a thin, flexible tube) fitted so that I could undergo peritoneal dialysis at home for nine hours every evening to keep me alive.

These thoughts were going round and round, but I brushed them away with thoughts of: "YAY!! It's a new start, I will feel better, I will have more energy, I will be more like me again." This helped me feel more positive but, hey-ho, I am only human, you know, and there were still some lingering doubts; I'm sure you can understand.

So back to the surgery, the radiologist introduced herself and saw I was smiling and laughing and that set the tone for the procedure. Very soon we were joined by my lovely nephrologist, who was to insert the catheter.

A very quiet, softly spoken man, he had been with me through my Polycystic Kidney Disease (PKD) journey for the past three years. It comforted me to see him there, with his lovely smile and interesting surgical gear on. All I can remember was some sort of army pattern and a yellow mask covered with a visor.

He began by placing the ultrasound probe on my belly and then he asked the nurse to push a button on the side of the machine. There was a slight pause and then he said, "Try that one," which didn't help to put me at ease.

The radiologist replied, "You shouldn't have to touch anything on the bottom there," and I started to giggle nervously. He continued, "It's not my usual operating room, so some of the equipment's new to me." I laughed some more.

"I have your machine here if you would rather use that," the nurse piped up and I said, "Thank God for that!" and laughed. They quickly hooked up the correct machine and it was time to start. The mood was fun and cheerful after that little introductory laughter session.

"Please don't knock me out," I asked the doctor and he agreed. The surgery was usually done with just a local anaesthetic and a sedative. He pushed down on my belly and said, "Sharp scratch." I took several deep breaths in and calmed my mind. I could feel the needle going in and a slightly uncomfortable pain. He did a few more of these as he moved up my belly.

My mask was obstructing my view, but I could see the x-ray in the distance. Watching the screen was a little difficult, so I opted to just close my eyes and breathe.

The nurse and radiologist kept checking in on me, "Are you okay, Jo-Dee?" they asked. To which I replied with a thumbs up or a: "Yes, fine thanks."

I was prompted to breathe deeply again when I saw the doctor holding what looked like a long piece of wire and heard him say, "This will be uncomfortable for about two minutes." It was at that point that he was inserting the tube into my peritoneal cavity.

I got another 'sharp scratch' warning and then the doctor said, "You are so brave, Jo-Dee, you are doing really well." Then he proceeded to tell the nurses and radiologist about my career as a laughter therapist and motivational speaker, and how I worked with businesses and helped people de-stress through laughter.

"Did you see how strong her mind is?" he asked. "That's proof of how good her techniques are. I didn't give her a sedative!"

While he was stitching me up, we began laughing and joking and I felt fine. Sure, I had some pressure on my belly, but I was good to go.

He gave me the good news that I could go home five hours early because I hadn't needed the sedative. That was amazing. The nurses were in shock when I returned and was told I could be discharged immediately.

And I said, "Well, that is all because I laughed my way through it…"

In this memoir, I want to take you on a journey of how I was able to get to that state and how *Laughter* became my *Lifeline*.

Chapter 2

Life on Stage (1990–2004)

A good laugh heals a lot of hurts
                                    Madeleine L'Engle

By the time I was in my early twenties, I had left South Africa, where I was born, and already fulfilled my dream of becoming a professional dancer. I was travelling the world, making fantastic money, meeting awesome people, just living the dream.

Being centre stage was the best feeling in the world, wearing diamanté costumes and feathers and having the audience glued to my every move gave me a huge rush and it was where I wanted to be…

Then BANG! I lost it – I got injured.

I was working in Macau where I used to do an Argentinian routine involving a lot of foot stamping and the French can-can, both of which place a lot of stress on the joints. Although the stage had a wooden surface, it was solid concrete underneath, and this exacerbated my injury. My left knee became swollen and very painful and I started to fall for no reason. The show's choreographer, knowing how much I loved my job as lead dancer and that I didn't want anyone taking my place, told me to get it checked out and not return to the stage until I had found out what was going on and received treatment.

So, off I went to Hong Kong, just a ferry ride away from Macau, and had an MRI scan of my knee, which revealed a 2-3cm diameter bone cyst. All that impact twice nightly (and three times on Saturdays!) was causing the hole in my knee to get bigger and my entire femur could have split had I continued. I was told that I would need to have it cut out and probably wouldn't be able to dance again. Little did I know that this would be the first of many cysts that I would encounter in my life; I think my parents were blowing bubbles when they made me!

I hadn't planned for my future nor saved any money. Without a back-up plan, I was alone and scared in Macau and suddenly overwhelmed by a deep depression.

So, I did what any normal depressed person would do and I went to the movies; I went to see *Amadeus*. I didn't realise at the time how this movie would change my life forever, but it sure did.

As you may know, Mozart was a genius at communicating through his music but not so good without it. The way he dealt with everything was to laugh. He laughed at everything and most of all he laughed at himself. I loved that idea and decided to do the same. I laughed at everything AND IT WORKED!!! (If you want to see a clip from the film, google *'Amadeus laughing'*, and I am sure you will giggle along too.)

I managed to get back on stage for a short time, doing easy routines, which gave me just long enough to be able to plan what I would do with my future. The laughter put me in a good mood and set me up for the next stage of my life. *'The show must go on,'* after all…

Life goes on – enter Enriqué

So, I carried on with life and its various ups and downs and got my wild child out of my system during ten crazy years (that would possibly make a book on their own). It was during that time that I met Majid in Athens, Greece. He was a model and had come to work for the agency I had started. Very soon we got together and it was a big love story. We travelled all over Greece, including the stunning islands of Rhodes and Crete, and had a ball. I supplied the dancers and entertainment to many of the clubs and therefore was always greeted with a bottle of vodka or something similar when I visited them. We had lots of fun and business was good.

After a few months, I found myself pregnant – something I had been told by my gynaecologist might not happen because I also had cysts on my ovaries. But my lovely son Enriqué was born in September 2003 after dancing in my belly, begging to come out a month prematurely.

What a beautiful boy he was, nicknamed 'Smiler' because he always had a big grin on his face. He was such a joy and the apple of my eye. I remember telling him that he was my world and how I would do anything for him. There is a very special bond between mother and son and that has never changed for us.

A couple of months before I gave birth, we moved into an amazing penthouse apartment with a view of the

Mediterranean Sea on one side and the Acropolis of Athens from the balcony on the other side. It was a dream house with all the mod cons you can think of.

Unfortunately, it soon became clear to me that Majid had a drinking problem. When I was in the clubs concentrating on business, I didn't notice the bottles of gin that he would polish off. Now, I am not a prude and can certainly do my fair share of drinking on occasions but since I was pregnant, I had stopped, of course. I mean, wouldn't you?

Majid continued to drink after Enriqué was born. We had started a clothing company that made stage costumes and the best time to visit the clubs to take orders and deliver finished outfits was usually after midnight. When I got home, I would often find Majid passed out with baby Enriqué on the bed wide awake.

Obviously this led to a bit of tension, plus on many occasions where he had been the one to go to the clubs on business, he would stay out drinking with my dancers, leaving me home alone to look after our baby. I had not had any experience with children and was really nervous. I can remember sitting in the bedroom all on my own while he was laughing and drinking with a few of my 'girls' on the balcony. This left me feeling scared, alone, inadequate and, of course, jealous.

Majid began to make a habit of going out every night and returning late, saying that he was watching our business. Very soon rumours started to fly around that he was having an affair. To this day he denies it, and I will never know for sure, but it made things really rocky between us.

On one particular occasion, things got so bad that he

wanted to hit me; I remember running into the street to get away from him and I called the police. That was the final straw for me, and I kicked him out.

He left and disappeared for a while, leaving me with a pile of debt and a business that was his brainchild. I had to move somewhere more affordable and sort things out. I had lost a lot of business when he took over while I was pregnant, and many clubs told me not to let him anywhere near them. Being an artist manager is not easy, it's like glorified babysitting!

I had managed to work with Mafia and strong men for years and never had a problem. The artists that worked for me were all professional, amazing and stunning to look at. I found it was a great advantage having been a professional dancer myself because it allowed me to push them to be the best they could be.

Running my business and working was difficult and I had a live-in nanny come to help me because I was out most nights. I did long for my happy family, but it seemed it was not going to happen.

I heard rumours that Majid was dancing in clubs and getting really drunk. His phone didn't work, and we had no contact for about four months, which was really upsetting.

Then one day I got a call from him saying he would like to see his son. Of course, I was delighted and agreed. When he came, he told me he had had a rough few months but decided to give up drinking. He had been sober for one month and felt much better.

I was really happy and we agreed he could see Enriqué whenever he wanted. Watching them together just melted my heart. Majid was very athletic and strong having been a world class judo champion. Enriqué would balance on one leg, standing on his father's hand, and Majid would then raise his arm so Enriqué was above his head. Once he was up there, Enriqué used to clap to encourage the people watching to applaud; it was so cute. Hehe, a showstopper like his mum.

Majid started coming around more often and even took Enriqué for the odd weekend. Things were good for a time.

I was working as a dancer doing a show with my best friend, Chez. It was a great job, our show was only eleven minutes long (a six-minute duo and my five-minute fire solo) and we usually did two clubs a night, three at the weekend. This left me free the rest of the time.

One night I was doing the shows on my own because Chez had gone away for a week. Usually I was full of energy and was known for the outrageous tricks I did on stage. But on this particular night I was not feeling very well. Actually, I had been under the weather for a while.

When I went to get paid after the show, the manager said, "I have watched you dancing for years and that was the worst performance you have ever done, are you okay? I'm sure there's something wrong with you." I told her I was not feeling well, and she insisted I went to the hospital.

By the time I got home, I was throwing up and had a temperature. Everyone was asleep so I went straight to bed. It was a very hard night for me and so at about 6am I decided to take a taxi and went to the duty hospital. I was really pale and weak but finally got to see someone and mentioned that I had Polycystic Kidney Disease (PKD), something that had been diagnosed a few years earlier. I didn't really know much about it, not having a regular GP, so I had just brushed it off.

For some reason, I was suddenly rushed into a ward and seen by a doctor. He had a look at me and asked, "Why did you wait so long to come in? You are in renal failure. If you had waited a few more days, you would have died." I had a cyst bleed and was really ill. They admitted me to hospital and put me on a drip with very strong medication.

Now, I hadn't told anyone where I was going because I thought I would be back in a couple of hours. How wrong was I?! And, as I had felt so ill, I hadn't charged my phone – oops! Of course, it died. There I was in hospital, hardly conscious, and nobody knew where I was. Well, I don't know about you, but I don't make a habit of memorising phone numbers, they are all stored in your phone, right?

So, no phone and no numbers, what was I going to do?

Luckily, I had my agent's business card in my bag and managed to ask someone if I could use the phone. I called her and asked her to contact Majid and tell him that I was in hospital and ask him to get Enriqué. He was still with his nanny, so all was good, but nobody had seen or heard from me in about twenty-four hours by this point.

I ended up spending nine days in hospital and at one point they told me in a very matter-of-fact way (only in Greece!) that I would need to have my left kidney removed because it was completely full of cysts, with the biggest being 9cm long. Thankfully the medication took effect after blowing out a few veins (hence the lovely episode trying to find a vein in chapter 1). It was a narrow escape but, after a week, things started to improve. YAY!!

This episode brought Majid and I closer again and we

got back together. Finally, my family was reunited. I was so happy. Majid was sober and a new person. He then said he would like to move back to Iran and see his family that he hadn't seen for four years. We had been chatting to them on Skype and they seemed lovely. I thought that it would be great to have the family all together.

The family meant everything to me, so I packed up my business, we sold everything and went to Iran.

Chapter 3

Life in Iran

If Laughter cannot solve your problems, it will definitely DISSOLVE your problems; so that you can think clearly what to do about them

Dr Madan Kataria

I can still remember arriving at Tehran Airport and being met by about ten people as we came out of the gate. It was amazing to see such love. There were tears and hugs and all these people coming up and kissing me. Luckily, I am good with people, so I lapped it up.

As we drove out of the airport heading home, wow! I was overwhelmed by the sight of cars everywhere; the roads were so busy, with lots of very old cars, beeping and honking, moving in all directions, and there didn't appear to be any traffic rules. Bear in mind that this was 2005 and since then a lot has changed, all the old cars have gone and been replaced by imported new ones.

When we got to Majid's parents' house, we put our stuff in the tiny room where we would be staying for the next few months. The house had a big lounge with a huge open space in the centre, covered with beautiful Persian carpets, and just a few chairs and sofas along the walls. I hadn't seen this arrangement anywhere else before, but I loved it.

Having all that space was great for the kids to play in, or for us to lounge in; dancing often took place there and then at mealtimes it was turned into a dining area by placing a *sofreh* (plastic tablecloth) on the floor.

Majid has seven brothers and sisters, who had all come to the airport to meet us, so together with their partners and kids, and Majid's parents, I think we counted twenty-one people in all. It was overwhelming having so many people around, but they were all so very lovely and welcoming. Iranian hospitality is just amazing.

On the second day, we were sitting in the lounge with the doors open because it was rather hot. As we were chatting, a falcon flew into the lounge and sat next to me. I was amazed, it seemed to be fixated on me. I asked if this was normal and they all answered, "No!" They were as amazed as I was!

Wow! What a welcome, and we took it as a good sign. The falcon would sit on my hand and eat the meat I gave it. I had bred birds when I was a kid, so I was used to handling them, but this was just fascinating. He didn't seem to like anyone else but me.

After allowing our visitor to stay a day, we thought it would be better to set it free in a nearby bird sanctuary. So, the family packed a picnic basket for about fifteen of us and we set off for the big release. I had tied a bit of string on his foot to keep him safe while we transported him, but he was as good as gold and just sat looking at me.

We sat on a blanket for a while as we decided

whereabouts to let him go. People were walking past and looking at this fine creature, which was so attached to this foreigner. When it was finally time to set him free, the string was released and I dropped my arm to encourage him to fly. It took a few attempts, but finally he understood it was time to go and away he flew, never to be seen again.

After four months, Majid and I got married and had a three-day wedding. We moved into an apartment of our own and life was good for about a year; I was really happy. Suddenly having a huge family was amazing, lots of people around all the time and I settled into my totally different life, Iranian style. Enriqué had lots of cousins, including a couple who were the same age as him.

I found a job as an English teacher (please don't tell anyone, my grammar is terrible!) and was working really hard, earning the money, while Majid stayed at home until he started studying. We started to drift apart but I really wanted another child so that my son would have a sibling and never be alone. Majid agreed and we started trying for a baby.

I fell pregnant a few months later and knew that I was from about two weeks. I started having lots of pain and bleeding. One night I remember that Majid and Enriqué had gone out and I was watching 'So You Think You Can Dance' on TV at home, alone, when I suddenly got this terrible pain and started bleeding non-stop.

I called Majid, crying, and he came straight back home with Enriqué to find what looked like a murder scene in the bathroom. I was lying on the floor in agony. I had big clots of blood coming out of me that looked like pieces of liver – sorry for those of you that are squeamish, but it really was a crazy spectacle.

We managed to get to the hospital and waited to see someone. When we did, they took one look at the blood and said, "I think you have lost the baby." They sent me off to have a D & C (which is a procedure that would have removed any remaining foetal tissue). However, when I got there, the doctor said, "You are still pregnant, and the baby is fine."

With a sigh of relief, I took the meds they gave me and was told that I would have to be on strict bed rest for the remainder of the pregnancy. I continued to bleed and was becoming increasingly nervous about the birth. I had had a few trips to the hospital during the first few months in Iran and didn't like it at all because of the language barrier. Although I was born and raised in South Africa, thanks to my dad I have a British passport, so I asked Majid if we could go to the UK to have the baby. I had spent time there previously and knew I would feel safer.

Chapter 4

Life in London

From there to here, from here to there, funny things are everywhere

Dr. Seuss

We left for London when I was five months' pregnant and rented a tiny room for the three of us in a shared house. I had promised Majid I would continue to wear my headscarf as I was his wife, not that I had a choice!

A few days after arriving in London, I managed to get a job at a call centre, working for a company that raised funds for charity. Yes, I'm sorry, it was me asking you to donate to Cancer Research, Oxfam, NSPCC and the National Trust.

Things with Majid and I were really rocky at this point. I was suddenly faced with a huge clash of cultures. I was in a country where I should have been free, yet living by Islamic law. It was really hard to handle.

Enter Fatimeh

One day, while I was calling for the Cancer Research 'Race for Life' project, I suddenly started feeling unwell and had severe cramps. I was barely seven months' pregnant, but when I was taken to hospital it turned out that my waters had broken, and I was ready to give birth.

I remember being really annoyed because I had bought myself a gift – a ticket to see 'Guys and Dolls' starring none other than Patrick Swayze, something I had dreamed about, hehe… but my daughter was not going to wait. I'm not sure if I have forgiven her for that yet. She could have waited a couple of weeks, surely!

Anyway, I was lying on the bed in agony when the doctor entered the room and walked over to me to shake my hand. I reached out and shook his hand and my scarf fell off my head. We went through the consultation and then he left.

Majid turned to me and had a real go at me: first because I shook the (male) doctor's hand, something prohibited in Muslim culture, and second because my headscarf fell off in front of a man. Majid was furious with me; he didn't care that I was in pain and maybe in trouble nor that our baby could have been at risk.

I told him to leave and that our relationship was over. How could he do that to me? I remember feeling scared and alone. I was already emotional because of my condition and now I had this to worry about. I had had enough; I had been working triple shifts to make money for our family because he couldn't work, and this is how he treated me.

My poor baby, as yet unborn, was so small that I needed to have steroid injections to help her grow for a couple of days before they could bring her into the world. I was not sure when I would see my Enriqué again or what would happen between Majid and me. To make things worse, it was 29th December 2006, almost New Year.

Fatimeh arrived on 2nd January 2007 and was a tiny little thing weighing only 1.96kg. She was kept in an incubator while I was recovering from my C-section. Majid had been back but was keeping his distance, just bringing Enriqué to see me and making sure all was okay. It was very cold between us and we didn't discuss anything.

Recovery was difficult, but mentally rather than physically. The doctor had noticed that I would pass out on the way to visit my daughter, who was in an incubator along the corridor, yet my scar was healing nicely. He asked me if anything was wrong and sent me to a counsellor. I mentioned that Majid and I had broken up and that I was unsure of the future.

In her incubator, Fatimeh needed to be fed through a tube in her nose. She was so tiny that it was really scary to touch her for fear of hurting her. Majid was really good with her, feeding her and taking care of her. He has always been great with kids. I was an emotional wreck.

I remember how she would smile when I stroked the bridge of her nose; it was the most beautiful thing in the world. And, of course, Enriqué was over the moon to have a baby sister. This is a love that was set in stone and a bond that would never be severed. YAY!! I made the right decision to have her.

The counsellor asked me if I wanted to keep Majid away from the baby, but I declined because he was such a good father, and I couldn't do that to my kids. So, I bit my lip and went home, not sure what was going to happen.

A week after the birth, I returned to work; there was

really no choice, I was the breadwinner and we needed the money. The manager asked me what I was doing back so soon. I explained to her that I had no option as I hadn't been employed for long enough beforehand to qualify for maternity leave. She asked for written confirmation that I had chosen to come back to work of my own accord.

A few days went by and I woke up in agony, so we called an ambulance and I was rushed to hospital, only to learn that there was a piece of placenta still inside me – strange seeing that I had been opened up during Fatimeh's delivery by C-section!

So, I was back in surgery having it removed. This time I was told not to return to work for at least a month. What stress, thank goodness I was at least able to get sick pay, if not maternity pay.

A couple of weeks later I was heading to the loo when my son pointed at me – I was covered in blood. It was so scary, and once again I found myself in the back of an ambulance and on the operating table. What?! Another 10cm of placenta was found – seriously? Did I really need this?!!

As I at last started to heal physically, Majid's and Enriqué's visas were coming to an end. Majid had made it clear that I was not going to keep my babies; I felt helpless with nothing to offer them, so I watched the three of them leave. I just packed the pain away and swallowed it, something I did a few times in my life. I didn't like to feel pain, so I hid it. Maybe it was something to do with 'The show must go on' motto that I lived my life by. But this time I was not on stage, this was my life. This was the first of many uncertain painful goodbyes I was to go through in the years to come.

The only thing I knew was how to buckle down and work hard. So, I managed to get promoted and took on two new positions in the same company, training and recruitment. I was working seventy-two hours a week and had to sign another letter saying I chose to work that many hours. My life was literally wake up, work, eat, sleep, repeat.

I managed to make a fair amount of money, but I was miserable. I would call Majid in Iran to find out about the babies and feel so empty. He told me that Enriqué missed me and my little Fatimeh was beautiful. This made me yearn to be with them again. He had got a new apartment and was set up and asked me to come back.

So I did.

Chapter 5

Life Back in Iran

He deserves Paradise who makes his companions laugh

Koran

Things were great for a bit. I started teaching English again and we had our little family. It was hard juggling teaching and being a mum but that was something I got used to and actually enjoyed. There is nothing that can take away the feeling of love that your children give you.

I had interaction with my students and Majid's family, who have been amazing from day one; their support has always been great and something I cherish. But life was lonely, especially for someone like me, used to performing for crowds, having loads of friends all over the world and generally being very social.

I enjoyed laughing with my students as I told them stories about things I needed to get used to in Iran. One of my favourite stories is one about the loos. Yes, you heard me! This was always a real art for someone like me. Picture this: I would be wearing a pair of leggings, over which I would have a floor-length skirt and on top of that a long-sleeved soft jacket, also down to the floor. The toilets in Iran were simply holes in the floor and actually needed a great deal of balance when using them. Now the funny part is knowing which items of clothing go up and what goes down whilst you are balancing. I would have the female students in stitches as I mimed what was going on and what I found so challenging. It was great watching them laugh at this strange foreigner and they really opened up to me after that. There were so many contradictions in Iran and it made me love the country.

As there were not many native English speakers locally, I found myself in demand and could fill a day with classes. It was great to be appreciated, which is something that was lacking at home. Majid and I started to drift apart again very soon, and he would just disappear with the kids and I would be home alone. Often, they would have gone to his parents' house for dinner and I was left with an empty fridge after a twelve-hour shift and a two-hour commute.

We started to argue a lot and my happiness had gone. I loved being with my kids, but Majid started talking about wanting a *sigheh*, which is a 'temporary marriage', also known as a 'pleasure marriage'. This meant he could have another woman as long as he had a contract. I was not at all happy with this suggestion, as you can imagine.

There I was, living in Iran in order to be a family, and now I had to put up with this? There was no way I was going to agree to that. Our arguments started to become worse and more frequent and the one that stands out was when Majid got so angry that my poor baby Enriqué, who was about six by then, was scared that Majid might hurt me. Enriqué turned to me, with tears in his eyes, and said, "Mommy, please go."

My heart broke; he was a real mommy's boy and loved me so much, but even at that age he knew that I didn't stand a chance against his father. The fights were often stupid and seemed to be a power struggle between Majid and me. If I asked Enriqué to do something, such as brush his teeth, for example, Majid would tell me to leave him alone and, quite often, that would lead to a bitter argument between us.

I remember walking to work in the snow with my iPod playing 'Total Eclipse of the Heart' and wondering what I was going to do. Where would I go? How could I live? I knew it would be impossible to keep the kids as, according to Iranian law, the father always keeps the children after a certain age.

There are a lot of things that happened between us that I don't need to go into in detail; I simply felt that I had reached the point where my situation was unbearable and without hope for the future.

The final straw was a seemingly trivial argument, which occurred when we were going to visit my sister-in-law with the kids. The weather was cold, it was snowing and Enriqué was wearing flip flops, so I said, "Enriqué, please put your shoes and socks on," to which Majid responded, "He is fine, leave him."

I remember falling silent as we drove to Maryam's house. She was Majid's older sister, very kind, deeply religious and considered close to God. On request she would perform a ritual which provides a Yes or No answer to a question that is known only to the person asking it.

25

Majid lived his life by this. I asked her to do it for me. After cleansing herself and then praying, she asked the Qur'an to give me the answer.

My question was, "Should I leave Majid and the kids?" and the answer was "Yes".

I made my choice according to Majid's beliefs and the answer I received. I then told him I wanted a divorce. Things had got so bad that the situation was impossible to stand any longer. I was unable to educate my kids and look after them when I was always told to keep quiet. Majid said that if I went easily then he would let me go, but if I made trouble for him or tried to take the kids, which was impossible anyway in Iran, he would refuse.

As you can imagine, my decision was to go quietly. We didn't tell anyone about the divorce until after the event, then, once all the paperwork was done, we told the family. And just a couple of weeks after Fatimeh's first birthday I had my last cuddle from my precious babies and left with only €1,000 and nowhere to go. God, I had no idea what was going to happen next.

Chapter 6

Life Without My Kids

Humour is laughing at what you haven't got when you ought to have it

James Langston Hughes

I chose to go to Greece because it was the last place I had lived; that was the problem with being a citizen of the world, I had no home. I soon found a job that would enable me to get by while I tried to sort my life out. It was not easy, but I had no choice, I needed to do whatever had to be done so that I would be able to visit my kids.

Eight months passed without seeing them and I was pining for them. Finally, Majid agreed that I could come and visit them. I started looking into hotels in Iran and discovered that not only were they very expensive, but they were not too keen on having a single female guest. Majid said that if I paid him €500 I could stay with them and he would look after me. I just wanted a way to see my kids, so I agreed. Who knew that this would become the only way I saw them throughout the years to come and that without paying Majid that amount each time, I would not be able to see them?

Funnily enough, I don't remember much about the first time I returned to Iran, apart from a terrifying five-hour journey to Shomal (in Northern Iran) that the four of us took along one of the most dangerous roads in the world. It was a narrow, very winding road through some really big mountains; there was a sheer wall of rock one side and a steep drop on the other, with traffic going in both directions.

Majid had rented a house for us all for the week I was going to be there. I remember it was wet and humid. Things were a little strange at first with the kids but very soon they warmed to me. Enriqué was the first one because he had spent the first five years of his life with me and knew me, but Fatimeh was still a little hesitant. I had left when she was only a year old, so it was hardly surprising, but that didn't make it less upsetting.

Things between Majid and me were tense, as you can imagine. I chose to keep quiet while he mentally and emotionally abused me. Without going into detail, he made me feel really useless in so many ways. I was so angry and sad that I wanted to return home early, but I didn't. I stuck out the full week for my babies. I had missed them so much: just hugging them and feeling their soft skin on my cheek was worth everything I had to endure.

That was pretty much how my visits would go for the next few years. I managed to see my kids every two to three months for a week. My relationship with them was getting better, although Fatimeh still remained distant, but Majid and I were not good. He had gone from being an alcoholic to being extremely religious and the subject of religion tended to dominate his conversation. Once I'd returned to the UK, it took me about two weeks to recover and feel myself again after putting up with Majid's insults and criticism followed by the pain of having to say goodbye to my kids at the airport. Leaving them tore my heart out every time. The only way I could get through it was to turn around somehow and, as I walked away from them, to cut my feelings as the tears welled up.

After a visit with the kids in 2011, I was feeling heartbroken and began that familiar spiral down into a dark lonely depression that I had experienced on and off for the past few years. I chose to retreat to South Africa so I could be with my sister Debbie. She was only too pleased to have me to stay as we had only recently become close. Debbie was my half-sister from my mother's side. We had not spent any time together as kids but had met after the death of our mother in 1987.

You would have never known we had not spent time together growing up because we were so similar; not in looks, I am tall and blonde, while she is petite and dark, but in what we thought and how we acted. It was wonderful to be with someone who loved me so much and she scooped me up off the floor and started to rebuild my confidence. We spent hours chatting and getting to know each other better and she was very supportive.

One day I was talking to Debbie about my dancing days and told her the story of watching the film *Amadeus* when I was in Macau, feeling depressed because I was injured. As I explained how I had tried Mozart's trick of laughing at everything and found it so helpful at the time, I realised that although I had tested his strategy and it had worked for me back then, I hadn't thought to use it again during my subsequent troubles many years later. "There is something in this laughter thing," I said, "I am sure I can help myself and many others with it."

"Google it," Debbie said.

And that is exactly what I did. I found information on how laughter could help with depression. There was also something out there called Laughter Yoga.

This fascinated me and after doing a bit of research I found that I was in luck; Dr Madan Kataria, the founder of Laughter Yoga, was coming to South Africa to do a Teacher Training course. Not only that, it was being held in Johannesburg, which is where I was staying at the time. YAY!! Talk about meant to be.

Becoming Licensed to Laugh

Dr Kataria told the story of how he started as a medical doctor and ended up becoming the laughter guru. He had been researching the benefits of laughter for an article in a journal he published. According to Dr Kataria, it all started with people like Dr Lee Berk, who concluded, after thirty years of research, that, "Laughter decreases stress hormones, improves the immune system and boosts endorphins."

Then there was Dr Norman Cousins, author of *Anatomy of an Illness*, who suffered from ankylosing spondylitis (a type of arthritis characterised by long-term inflammation, and often fusion, of the joints of the spine), which left him in almost constant pain. Believing in his body's own natural resources and the healing power of the mind, he wanted to take charge of his own health and decided to expose himself to a continuous stream of humourous films and similar 'laughing matter'. He later claimed that ten minutes of belly rippling laughter would give him two hours of pain-free sleep when nothing else, not even morphine, could help him.

Dr Kataria went on to tell us about Dr Patch Adams, who is the subject of a film starring Robin Williams. I think it's a great movie and highly recommend that you watch it! Patch believed that patients would recover faster if a fun, happier, more colourful bedside manner was used. So, he started wearing a clown nose when he saw patients and playing jokes on them, and found that he was right.

I was sucked into this because it was based on evidence from medically qualified doctors and I lapped up all the information that was being given. Then Dr K, as I like to call him, described how he had been so inspired by these findings that one day in 1995, in Mumbai, India, he arranged a meeting in a park with his wife and three friends and the five of them started to tell jokes. Of course, you know what happens when you tell jokes... you laugh, right?

Everyone had such a great time that they decided to meet daily and their group soon grew as it became the talk of the town. But something strange happened when they reached about fifty people. The jokes started to get a bit racist, sexist and every other '-ist' there was known to humans. There was no longer that positive feeling.

Dr K resolved to consider the problem overnight and said that he would have the answer in the morning. This is where the magic happened; based on the scientific evidence he had studied, which demonstrated that simulated laughter

31

and real laughter provide the same benefits, Laughter Yoga was born.

"What is Laughter Yoga?" Dr Kataria explained, "It's a simulated exercise, done in a group and with eye contact very soon changes to real laughter." Can you believe that what started out with five people in a park is now practised in over one hundred and ten countries and has thousands of laughter clubs around the world?

We learned about the benefits of laughter and then went on to learn the laughter exercises. All I know is that my belly hurt because I had been laughing for five days straight. The feeling of being on a high carried on for days and I knew that I had found my calling.

I am forever grateful to Dr Madan Kataria for giving me this amazing gift of laughter and I have had the pleasure of sharing it with thousands of people over the years.

Inspired by my newfound skill, I rushed to gather a group of people to hold my very first laughter session on my own. My sister and her family had a diving concession in Mozambique and we had gone there for a holiday. Perfect, laughter on the beach, YAY!! I couldn't wait. Luckily, my sister's company 'Simply Scuba' had a great open space on their site, where the divers collected their gear before diving. All I needed now was a group of people to give it a try.

And on that hot summer's day, 'Simply Laughter' was born. The group of fifteen was a mixture of friends, family and clients of all ages and Debbie was the official camera lady. The excitement and nerves set in and I felt as if I was going to burst.

Oh my gosh! I did it, the group laughed and had fun

as we started with an introductory clapping exercise, then moved on through something like twenty foundation exercises. It worked, and I was over the moon. Having been a dancer helped me explain the exercises and my energy was contagious, I was told.

I then practised Laughter Yoga with anybody I could find; I had a group of kids, namely my nephew and niece and their friends, who were all roped into my newfound game, but the best thing I learnt was to laugh alone every day. That ability, to laugh alone, is what has enabled me to laugh during adversity.

Tip: Practise laughing alone every day and you will find it easier to laugh in difficult situations.

Something changed inside me, I was starting to feel so much better and suddenly I had a feeling that I needed to know even more about this transforming power of laughter, and everyone else had to know about it too. That's when I decided to move to Dubai where I would pursue my new career as a laughter facilitator, running my own company, 'Simply Laughter Worldwide'.

Chapter 7

Life in Dubai

*The human race has one really effective weapon,
and that is laughter*

Mark Twain

I left the sale of my nearly-new (I had only been in South Africa about eight months) household goods to my sister Debbie; this would provide the money I needed to set myself up in Dubai. Debbie was amazing! After advertising on Gumtree, she very soon had a buyer and managed to sell everything to the same person. She got a copy of the bank deposit slip, a copy of his ID, she really went all the way.

The buyer was due to pick everything up at 8am South African time, which was 10am Dubai time. I had been looking at all the paperwork Debbie had sent me and when I clicked on the buyer's ID, I saw I could move the photo – oh dear – it was a fake!

I tried desperately to get hold of Debbie on any platform available. We usually used all of them at various times, but this time I couldn't contact her by any means. OMG – I didn't know what to do. I had no way of warning her about the scam.

So, putting into practice my renewed decision to laugh in the face of adversity, I took myself to Ibn Battuta Mall and started walking with my phone to my ear and just laughed. I walked up and down to defuse the emotional turmoil I was going through. I was angry, afraid that I was about to lose all the money I had, irritated by having to deal with this setback, frustrated at not being able to communicate with Debbie by any method, you name it, but I managed to laugh it out.

Finally, my sister called me saying, "I've been trying to get hold of you all morning to see if you got the money, but I couldn't get through before now. He came to collect your stuff; he's taken all of it." I laughed and said, "The money didn't go through, Deb. I was trying to contact *you* to tell you it was a scam." Bless her, she was horrified, but I just laughed and said, "Don't worry about it, Deb, he obviously needed it more than I did."

Being a rather stubborn, hard-working individual, and without my anticipated startup funds, once I arrived in Dubai, I worked day and night marketing the company and my services. I started a group on Meetup and within days of opening my account I was contacted by someone from *Yogalife* magazine wanting to write an article about me. I was also asked to do an interview for the show 'Out & About' on Dubai One, an English-language TV station.

On the course with Dr Kataria in Johannesburg, we had learned how important it is to laugh every day, doing various laughter exercises so that laughing becomes a natural habit. "You don't laugh because you're happy, you're happy because you laugh," is how Dr K summed it up for us. I also knew from my own experience during the twenty years that had elapsed between watching *Amadeus* in Macau and retreating to South Africa on the brink of depression that being aware of the power of laughter, and even making the decision to adopt the strategy of responding with laughter, was not enough on its own. 'Live Life Laughingly' is a great motto, but to do so requires practice. With that in mind, I started doing weekly laughter yoga sessions free of charge and as the group grew, so did my followers. It was very rewarding to hear from people about how they felt so much better.

In 2012 I had the opportunity to attend a business Laughter Yoga course at the All America Laughter Yoga Conference in Chicago. The course was given by Merv Neal, a multimillionaire businessman who, ten years previously, just days after retiring at the age of forty-five, had been diagnosed with a life-threatening disease and given weeks to live. On hearing the news, Merv saw the funny side of having worked so hard to become successful only to be given weeks to live, and laughed. He got his affairs in order, and laughed. He planned his funeral, and laughed. He continued to laugh and actually started to get better until he reached the point where his doctors gave him the all-clear. Merv Neal was living proof that laughter worked; what an amazing mentor.

The information that Merv shared with me became my foundation for helping many corporate businesses subsequently. It was invaluable being able to combine the experience of someone from a corporate business background with everything that I had learned from Dr Kataria. There is a big difference between the laughter yoga seen in parks and what is needed and valued in a business setting. Merv also taught me how to craft and give a talk for large groups of people and showed me how my story could help others.

Several months later, on 13th February 2013, my birthday as it happens, the first media coverage of me as a Laughter Yogi was about to take place; it was both exciting and nerve-racking. A group of us had agreed to be filmed and we waited for the hosts of the show 'Out & About', Punam Verma and Layne Redman, who were running late because they had had a tyre blowout, like really. What bad luck. When they arrived, they were a bit shaken up and really needed to laugh. It was great fun and you can see the show here https://youtu.be/6_zJJG9Slhg

This was actually the start of a wonderful friendship with Punam; she really helped me during my time in Dubai, for which I am very grateful.

Very soon after that, I started doing paid corporate gigs for some amazing companies like Benefit Cosmetics Middle East, Yassat hotel group and Qatar Airways, which allowed me to earn enough money to go and visit my kids in Iran. The first time I visited them since making laughter part of my life, I remember my kids running up to me in Tehran Airport and giving me that amazing hug I always got when I returned. By now you must have realised that Majid was not big on compliments or saying nice things to me, right? Well, this time he took one look at me and said, "What have you done, you look so young and beautiful?"

"Hehe," I answered, "I have started laughing. It's my new business." He replied, "Keep doing whatever it is because it's working."

I was gobsmacked, especially coming from him.

Somehow, I knew this trip was going to be different. It turned out to be really transformational for many reasons. One day, when the kids were out playing with their cousins and I was alone with Majid, I had the chance I had been waiting for. On my many courses I had learned a new technique called 'Gibberish', which I really wanted to try with Majid. By disrupting the brain patterns associated with continual inner verbalisation, gibberish provides relief from turbulent emotions and from the chattering mind. The result is to feel more calm, relaxed and creative. As you have already seen, my relationship with my ex was toxic. There was so much I needed to say to him but hadn't been able to for fear of what he might say or how he would react. I knew that carrying the hurt and pain without expressing it was not good for me and I hoped that gibberish would enable me finally to let it all out, safely, without making things worse.

So, I tried it on him. I asked him to sit down and listen to me, and not to interrupt me, and please to just give me the chance. I went into detail about being let down, abandoned, how I was afraid of losing my kids, how heartbroken I was. I said all this in a non-existent language he couldn't understand.

What do you think it did for me? I released all the built-up negativity, I told him how I felt, and I let it go. It was the best thing I could have done. He looked a bit confused but didn't say anything. I think the emotion in my voice was evident. I ended with a laugh, and he laughed too. I said, "Thank you," and since then we have been able to tolerate each other and have a laugh. It seemed to break the ice and pain that had been hanging over us.

TIP: This works for personal and business problems; sometimes you may need to say it to the mirror, but get it out. Why don't you try it?

See APPENDIX 1: Benefits of Gibberish Meditation

The trip continued to go well and there was a birthday celebration for the kids. We had gathered with the family and there were about twenty-five people sitting around the *sofreh* (plastic tablecloth) having a meal.

Enriqué decided to jump over the *sofreh* and managed to kick a watermelon, which went splat on the wall. He stopped in horror and looked at me. The old me would have screamed, "Enriqué, what have you done? You know you shouldn't jump over the *sofreh*!" leaving him feeling embarrassed and upsetting everyone there.

Instead, the new me said, "Ha, ha, ha, Enriqué, good shot!" He turned around to me with his mouth open in shock and said, "Sorry, Mom," then ran off to fetch something to clean it up. Everyone laughed with me and everything was fine. After all, it was really no big deal, was it? I learned a huge lesson from that incident and used it subsequently in many areas of my life.

TIP: Don't sweat the small stuff, laugh at it.

Majid began to tell everyone that I had started a new business, which was all about laughter. People were curious and wanted to give it a try. Neighbours and families took part and it was great fun. One of the kids that came along back then has continued to repeat one of my catchphrases, "Very good, very good, YAY!!" to me every time he sees me, although he doesn't speak or understand English. It is amazing how the phrase has anchored in his brain. Apparently, all the kids have been laughing about it for years.

This time my goodbye was not so difficult, it was filled with hope for the future. We had had such a great time and somehow there had been a great shift, for which I was very thankful.

I returned to Dubai with my love tanks filled, ready to change the world one laugh at a time. The word was spreading about my laughter sessions and I was booked to do three classes a week at the Holistic Institute. This was great experience; the more sessions you do, the more you learn, the more people you help and the more you find out how much laughter is needed.

After running a session for Qatar Airways, I was given a return ticket to anywhere in the world. The Canadian Annual Laughter Conference was being held in Toronto, so I used my ticket to go to that.

Wow! Can you imagine three hundred Laughter Yogis together laughing for a few days nonstop? In Dubai I was pretty much the only one practising Laughter Yoga, so this was a real treat for me. It was there that I met some of the great Master Trainers and seasoned facilitators. It was a dream come true. Dr Kataria was there too, and it was great to dance and laugh with him. I am grateful for so many solid friendships that started at that conference.

This solidified my choice of profession, I loved it and I knew I was doing the right thing. Plus, my own personal well-being had improved so much, I was living proof that laughter was the best medicine.

Chapter 8

Life with Another Burst Cyst

God has a smile on His face
Psalm 42:5

I had spent a month in Canada staying with a good friend of mine, Cheryl, who very kindly hosted me. We had been friends since meeting in Dubai at a social event, she was always there for me and supported me in so many ways. One thing is sure, I am blessed with many friends around the world.

I was called back to Dubai to help as speaker liaison for an event with some of the top speakers and authors around at the time; Jack Canfield, the co-creator of the *Chicken Soup for the Soul* book series and author of *The Success Principles*; Marshall Goldsmith, one of the top business coaches in the world; the late Tony Buzan, who invented 'Mind Mapping' and Ron Kaufman, considered the number one global customer service guru.

It was while watching Jack Canfield run his one-day workshop to over three hundred delegates that I knew I wanted to do the same thing. Everyone was captivated by every word he said, he was such an inspiration.

I was lucky enough to help him a bit at that event, and I told him that I would really love to be a speaker like him. "You already are, Jo-Dee, just believe it," he replied. That was something that stuck with me for years, not only the message, but the fact that he had remembered my name.

With my new ambition in mind, I started networking wherever I could in order to be seen. I was looking for a chance to speak to bigger audiences than I was currently. Being the workaholic that I am, I was at BNI (Business Networking International) meetings at 6.45am and other networking events in the evening – plus a few during the day!

I was mixing with successful people, mega-rich people and one day I was in a room at the top of the Burj Khalifa, the world's tallest building at the time, with a handful of people whose combined net worth was several billion dollars. It was a very exciting day, but I started to feel tired and when I later saw a photo posted on Facebook taken at that event, I could see that I was as white as a sheet.

Within a couple of days, I was unable to move and I started bleeding extensively; there was blood in my urine, I had bloody diarrhoea, I was losing blood as if I was having my period and I was vomiting blood. It was summer, when the temperature in Dubai can reach fifty degrees, and many people go away because the heat is just too much to bear. Luckily, I was in my air-conditioned hotel apartment, but because I felt so ill, I was not able to work and that meant I wasn't earning any money.

I was like that for a few weeks, then suddenly I became worse and couldn't even eat for ten days. I had a very high temperature and was in so much pain that all I could do was just lie there, too weak to do anything.

A few months earlier, I had become friends with an amazing therapist, called Gulnara, who had introduced me to the concept of our minds being able to play tricks on us and the power of the subconscious mind. I had already seen for myself how laughter could change both mindset and mood. Gulnara was helping me with a few issues I had been having, mainly to do with money, and she often said that I was the only client of hers who actually did their homework and much more additional reading besides.

I found that the more I read, the more I felt I had to learn. I was particularly interested in the use of affirmations (positive statements to help overcome self-sabotaging and negative thoughts) and EFT (Emotional Freedom Technique), also known as tapping, which is an alternative self-help therapy for physical pain, anxiety, emotional distress and post-traumatic stress disorder (PTSD), amongst other conditions. The tapping process is done in order to reduce physical tension and promote a deeper mind-body connection. When Gulnara heard that I was so ill she very kindly came over with some soup and did a few sessions with me. She also told me about the author Louise Hay, and I listened to her books *You Can Heal Your Life* and *You Can Heal Your Body*.

As time went on, I became weaker from not eating properly. I finally managed to get myself to the hospital to be told that, once again, I was not in very good shape and I would need to be admitted. Now I didn't have medical insurance, nor did I have enough money to pay the crazy health care prices in Dubai, so I went back to my hotel apartment. Gulnara came to me there and said, "Jo-Dee, it is now between you and God." Having introduced me to techniques to help me, she felt that there was nothing more anyone else could do.

I had not seen my kids for about four months, and I was pining for them, but I didn't have the funds to see them. I felt really scared and didn't know what to do. Then a friend of mine lent me some money and I had a choice – either to go into hospital or go to visit my kids. Wow – what a choice! Gulnara had told me not to waste money on going to hospital, just go and see my kids. I had no idea how I would make the journey, I was so weak after losing such a lot of blood and not eating for ten days.

But, somehow, a little fire lit in my heart at the thought of seeing the kids. I managed to drag myself to the airport and to Iran. Majid's brother picked me up and took me to his parents' house. I remember Majid's mother took one look at my pale complexion and my frail body and she said, in Farsi, "You need to eat!"

She was amazing, she spoon-fed me soup every hour, knowing that because I had not eaten for so long, I was finding it hard to keep anything down. She said, "The kids are coming tomorrow so you have time to get well."

Although my Farsi was limited, I found I could communicate with her easily. All it takes is an open heart, trust and the will to be understood. We had got on well from the first day I met her. Even Majid's father had said to me, back when Majid and I had first begun to have relationship problems, "I don't care what is going on with you and Majid, but you are now my daughter and always will be, you are welcome in my house anytime." How amazing is that? It's also very rare.

I am so grateful to Majid's family for standing by me

and especially to his mum for nursing me, so that I would not scare my kids! Whatever she gave me to eat seemed to settle my stomach and stayed down. I managed to brighten up a bit by the time the kids arrived. YAY!!

I would listen to Louise Hay when I had a moment to myself and made the effort to use her affirmations. For the time being I was with my kids, and their love is what healed me. They were so full of love and laughed a lot, as I had taught them. They would even remind *me*, "Hey, Mom, it's okay, just laugh!"

Fatimeh said, "Don't worry, next time you come, and we pick you up from home (the airport) we will stop at the pharmacy so you can get medicine." She was too adorable, she thought I lived in the airport and she now knew I needed medicine. How cute is that?

One thing I learned from Louise Hay was that every physical pain has an emotional connection. Kidneys are connected to feelings of regret and fear. Well, that certainly was true, I regretted not being with my kids and I was fearful for the future and this was something I would spend a long time working on.

After eight days with my kids, I returned to Dubai and continued to work on healing on many levels. One exercise I did that really worked for me was a forgiveness exercise (See Appendix 2). This really helped me and I did it many times. Once you realise that everyone is as scared as you are, going through life, it kind of shifts something in you. This opened up a new way of looking at people for me; becoming aware that I was not the only one led me to always think the best of people and to give them the benefit of the doubt.

I worked these ideas into my laughter classes and found that they enhanced them. Another idea that I incorporated I learnt from reading Jack Canfield's book, *The Success Principles*, in which he says that by accepting that you are responsible for all that happens in your life, because of the choices you make, you are able to be in control of your life.

This then led me to doing a course in Clinical Hypnotherapy. Oh boy, did this blow my mind! We covered so many different methodologies within the course, it was amazing. I was determined to fill my life with joy and 'find my happy' and share this with as many people as I could.

On the course we learned about graphology, how your signature can reveal a lot about you and how changing it can help you. EFT was also covered, which I had delved into before, but it was great to see how it was used with hypnotherapy. This is where I also learned the importance of the way we speak to ourselves (our self-talk).

Have you ever paid attention to what you say to yourself? Wow, this really shocked me; I often made fun of myself, but actually by doing that I was reinforcing a negative opinion of myself over and over again. Having learnt that when we speak in metaphors it gives amazing insight into what we are really feeling, I naturally went on to do a course in Metaphor Therapy!

Metaphor therapy is a great way to see what is really going on in your subconscious mind. It involves drawings and analysing what you are saying. Once you get to the bottom of what you are really saying, you are able to make a few tweaks and change it. This was something new and hadn't yet reached the UK.

I spent my time researching, reading and watching

videos on so many different things. My days were filled with signing my name over one hundred times, writing my affirmations, watching lots of motivational videos, monitoring what I said and a lot more besides. I was on a mission! I wanted things to change and I was determined to make it happen, so I dedicated all my time to pursuing that goal, using every methodology I could lay my hands on.

BUT I found myself miserable because I was not getting the results I had hoped for. Crushed and demotivated, I went to my hypnotherapy teacher and said, "Irina, it's not working, I am doing it all and things are worse than before. What am I doing wrong?"

She asked me what exactly I was doing, and I told her the long list. She just laughed at me and said, "Jo-Dee, just stop everything, now!" She said I was pulling myself in too many directions at once and needed to slow down, choose one thing and focus on that for the moment. She suggested I just concentrated on one affirmation for a couple of weeks: "What can I do today that can make things far better than I could imagine?"

I took her advice and found myself relaxing and able to do more without my mind spinning out of control with too much pressure. Have you ever done that? Wanted to make a change so badly that you tried all the different techniques together and in the end it either didn't work or you didn't know which one was responsible for the improvement?!

Tip: The best way to find out what works for you is to take a mix 'n' match approach, trying exercises from different methods and adopting those that seem to produce the desired result. Not everything works for everyone.

Combining various methodologies works well for me, but the mix of exercises varies depending on what the issue is. I found it really interesting experimenting with different combinations, one of which, laughter and hypnotherapy, later became a practice called 'Laughnosis', developed by Dave Berman and James Hazlerig, two of my laughter buddies.

Another combination I enjoyed was laughter and EFT or tapping. Laughter is a great way to break through our critical filter and helps us access the subconscious where our mental blocks and 'corrupt files' are kept.

Even doing mirror work, which I learnt from Louise Hay and Robert Holden, was so much easier and effective when combined with laughter. We may be told to love ourselves or to say positive things to ourselves, but this can be hard in the beginning when you don't believe them; I certainly had that problem. When I started laughing at the same time as saying, "I love you, Jo-Dee," to my reflection in the mirror, it made it easier and seemed to have good results.

Life is like a yo-yo and there will always be ups and downs and things that work and things that don't. The way I see it is that, like a yo-yo trick, you can use the downs to lift you up again. Have you ever seen the yo-yo trick 'Around the World'? Well, it starts with spinning the yo-yo down and then using that energy to provide the momentum necessary to complete the circle. This is how I see life. What can I learn when I am down? How did I get there? What were the triggers? What can I do differently to prevent it happening again? Once all this had occurred to me, wallowing in self-pity was no longer an option for me because I knew that just kept me depressed.

This was a big lesson. For so many years I had told my story of how I lost my kids and felt like a victim, but after lots of work on myself I told my story to inspire other people to 'find their happy'. I noticed I was inspiring people rather than getting them to feel sorry for me. This made me feel amazing and I healed more and more by practising what I had learned.

Chapter 9

Life as Events Director

As soon as you have made a thought, laugh at it
Lao Tsu

As I was growing as a person, working on my inner demons and helping the odd clients, I longed to be a speaker on the stage like the authors I had seen during the previous couple of years.

My finances were still unstable because I didn't have a work visa; it was really expensive for me to buy one and I was just starting my business. Most of my money went on travelling to see my kids and paying my rent. One of the main things I needed to work on was my relationship with money. Then, out-of-the-blue, I was offered a job as Events Director with a company that ran international conferences among other activities, in addition to promoting authors and speakers. They say spend time with those doing what you want to do, so I was delighted. I was offered a small salary, plus commission, and the opportunity to take time off to continue working with my clients. The company gave me my work visa and said they would also promote me as a speaker.

This was really exciting and – with my usual workaholic approach – I dived right in and was so happy. I mean, who wouldn't want to rub shoulders and get up close to these great thought leaders? Brian Tracy, Tony Buzan and Marshall Goldsmith to name but a few.

I was found an apartment in the same building where the owners of the company lived, which was also close to the office. This made things easier for transport as we were going to be working many long hours. The rent was more than half my salary, but I felt that was okay because I was sure I would make money on commission.

We used to have corporate breakfast events with about three hundred to five hundred delegates in attendance. Many of them were invited free of charge because they were upper management and decision makers. The idea was to let the delegates see the speaker in action so that they would then be likely to book them for their own in-house events or AGMs. We offered them a great breakfast and the chance to network, so we found that these events were usually well attended.

I loved the hustle and bustle of the event, with everyone excited to watch these greats on stage, and then jostling to try to get an autograph and photo with them. Can you imagine controlling a crowd of that size to accomplish all this within a tight timeframe?

But that was my job and I thrived on it. One day, Tony Buzan was the speaker, and it was even busier than usual. I took the mic and managed to get them all to line up against the wall and made the crazy line up work. I was laughing and joking with everyone in the lines so that they didn't feel it was a chore. A minute or two later, it was like a well-oiled machine and everyone was happy. Afterwards, Tony said to me, "I have never seen anyone control a crowd so fast and make it so much fun." We laughed together and went on to our next gig.

This one was easier. It was a group of about thirty CEOs with lunch provided. We had arrived a bit late because of the demand at the end of the first event but were there in time for when they started serving lunch. Tony needed a few minutes to gather himself and to chat before he ate; then just as they served him, he was called to give his talk.

As Events Director my eyes were on everything. I noticed his phone was running low, so I took it out of his bag and charged it. Tony had a very specific diet and as he had not been able to eat before his talk, I asked the chef to prepare a new plate and to make sure it would be ready in about forty-five minutes when his talk ended. Once Tony had finished and had pictures taken with the delegates, I apologised to the crowd and said that they could network for a bit while he had his lunch. Poor man, he had been on the go since about 7am without eating.

Everyone was happy with that plan and the delegates at his table were able to chat to him while he was having his lunch. After everyone had gone, Tony pulled me aside and asked, "How does a little dancer manage to pay so much attention to detail?" He said that I was the best manager he had ever had in thirty years, and he had noticed all the little things I had done for him, like charging his phone, organising fresh food for when he'd finished and even ordering his favourite coffee. He then gave me a rose. That started a tradition: from then on, every time we saw each other, he would always give me a rose. How lovely, and he was amazing to work with; most people were a little afraid of him because he knew what he wanted but... so did I!

We worked together on a number of occasions. One I remember in particular was not actually my event, but the company that I worked for also acted as his agent and Tony always requested me to look after him regardless of who booked him. I arrived at the event early as usual, I wasn't running it, so I needed to familiarise myself with everything. I found out his timing and all the other details, then waited for him at the entrance to the conference centre.

Tony happened to arrive at the same time as the Attorney General from DED (Department of Economic Development) and the usual VIP welcome was about to start. I'm not sure if you have seen one, but picture a long line of people waiting as the VIPs start walking through and shaking hands. After giving me the usual hug and kiss on the cheek, Tony and I stood there to watch the procession. But instead of walking between the two rows of people waiting for him and his entourage, the Attorney General made a beeline for me: he had seen me on stage a couple of weeks before doing my laughter talk, where I made five hundred Emiratis laugh at an event to celebrate the Business Excellence Awards. He came over, followed by a few other VIPs, shook my hand and introduced me to the other VIPs as the 'Laughter Lady'. It was the strangest thing that had ever happened; I then turned around and introduced them to Tony Buzan. We were both invited to walk in with them and join them in the VIP room. What fun, the event went well, and of course I made sure Tony got his Arabic coffee with dates that he loved. I have so many fond memories of him.

Unfortunately, Tony passed away in 2019, otherwise I would have asked him to do the foreword for this book. When I told him that I was moving to London, he tweeted, "London will be a much happier place now with Jo-Dee Walmsley."

During my time as Events Director in Dubai, I would often have an event starting early in the morning, which meant that I had to be there at 6am, after being up until late the evening before setting it all up. Then in the evening, once the event had finished, I would have networking events to attend. It was important to me to do my job well, so I was doing whatever I could, above and beyond my job description, and very soon the bosses learned to rely on me to do everything.

Another memorable event was one with Ron Kaufman. We had some major problems with the venue and had spent days sorting it out. Ron was very professional and particular about how things needed to run, rightly so. He knew I was in charge of running the event and things kept going wrong. My team was not really doing as well as usual because we had been let down at short notice and were a person short. This meant that I was running around trying to cover and do two jobs at once. This made me laugh, and the client that we were organising the event for sat me down for a coffee and asked, "How can you experience all this stress and still laugh?" I answered, "I only get through it *because* I laugh." We were all laughing at that when an Emirati lady came and joined us; it turned out that she was a member of the Royal Family and she asked me to please come and do a laughter session for her staff. It is amazing how people find you.

Soon after I started working for the company, I noticed that one of my bosses had some severe anxiety and depression problems. Something had happened in the past and he was not able to move on. Things were not going too well in the business either. There were days when he couldn't go to work because he just couldn't get out of bed. I would get a call and usually managed to get him to shift into a more positive mindset by using EFT on him to change his state of mind. It wasn't true healing as such, but had enough of an effect to get him up and off to work. We would also go into the park and laugh; I tried various techniques with him and managed to make a few changes, but we didn't spend enough time on it. I was always brought in to be a quick fix rather than to tackle the main problem.

This went on for months, putting a lot of pressure on me because I had to do his work too. He had lost his edge and was the one with all the connections. Whatever had happened in the past had affected the business too. He had lost many customers and big clients. This was something I had no idea about before joining the company. I was working so hard to make things improve and I did okay, but the company appeared to be in deep trouble and seemed to have so little money that we had to barter for many business essentials. Our printing, audiovisual equipment, designs, promo gifts, etc. were paid for with tickets to our events, and with other complimentary tickets for certain delegates the company was left with only about 20% of the available tickets actually paid for. As you can imagine, that particular business model didn't really work too well!

I still managed to see my kids every few months, which was great, but the cost of travel to Iran, having to pay Majid

€500 each time, plus the high rent in Dubai, didn't leave me much money for the twenty hours a day I was working. At first, I was okay with it because I was meeting amazing people, but it very soon started to take its toll on me. I didn't even have enough to take myself out for a dinner, not that I had the time! Not only that, but I was not making any commission from sponsorship as I had been led to expect, because there *was* no sponsorship. I didn't have time to supplement my income by doing paid laughter and other therapy sessions because I was working flat out trying to keep the company afloat, and I had fewer opportunities to speak than I'd hoped for. These were issues that I brought up with my bosses, also taking the opportunity to highlight how important it was for me to be seen on stage.

Chapter 10

Life's Ups and Downs

If you would not be laughed at, be the first to laugh at yourself

Benjamin Franklin

Luckily, after letting my bosses know how I felt, a few speaking gigs did come up and I started doing events for crowds of three, four and five hundred people. Then an email came in to my boss (I was Bcc'd in all his emails so I could follow them up) asking for speakers for the Toastmasters AGM. I saw who he proposed and said I wanted to be included. He agreed, and I went off to my kids for a visit, receiving the relevant emails on my phone while I was in Iran. The person making the decision replied to my boss with a comment next to each option: next to my name she wrote, "Nice to have but not essential."

I was fuming when I read this, so I pressed 'reply' and let my boss know that I was tired of not being promoted in such a way that would make people consider my message as essential. I went on to talk about how I helped with stress and depression and could enable businesses to create a healthier, happier place to work. I really told him straight, then pressed 'send' and continued enjoying my time with my kids.

Almost immediately my phone started pinging on WhatsApp and it was my boss saying, "What have you done? You sent this message to the client!" Oops! I laughed to myself. I was slightly in shock; I hadn't realised I had pushed 'send to all'. I was just about to apologise to him when an email came back from the client. She said, "I want Jo-Dee, if she is that passionate about her talk, she has to be good."

I apologised to my boss but couldn't resist saying that everything had worked out. Hehe, he laughed and said I was very lucky. I was so excited because I was going to be speaking in front of my biggest audience yet, eight hundred people. Not only would there be so many of them, but they were all Toastmasters: that meant they were used to giving feedback and would be really critical. Previously I had done a talk in Bahrain to a small local group of Toastmasters and one lady had found it necessary to correct me on a few things. Fortunately, I didn't pay too much attention to her criticism, as I was a professional speaker trained by some of the best. She had said I moved too much, but my subject matter was different from all the others and my talk involved a lot of audience participation; I was hired to get the audience up on their feet and moving! The head Toastmaster had understood and shut her up by saying that it was all relevant to my talk.

The other professional keynote speaker they had chosen was Jairek Robbins, whose father, Tony Robbins, is considered by many to be one of the world's top motivational speakers. Jairek resembles him in many ways and has his own inspirational story. I was in my element! My bio and photo were published alongside his in a feature that appeared in the international Toastmasters magazine. This was going to be my biggest challenge yet and I was so excited. It was also going to be the first time that the events company I worked for represented me as a professional speaker. The bosses had seen me do little bits on stage but never my full one-hour presentation. I had done it many times before, of course, just not for them. It was amazing getting a five-star hotel room on my own and being given the perks that you get as a speaker; I was also running a few things at the event, so I had to double up workwise, but I didn't care.

My picture was up all over the venue and people wanted my autograph and to have their pictures taken with me. I could feel my nerves building throughout the morning. I was on after lunch. Eating was something I couldn't ever do before speaking, I needed my energy to give to the crowd, not to digesting my food. I went in to do the sound check – I was my own manager! – and my bosses were nowhere to be found. But hey ho, I was getting the chance I wanted, and nothing was going to stop me. Then the room started filling up after lunch and it was time to go into action.

As I waited in the wings to make my entrance, the sound technician came and changed the battery of my lapel mic. The compère started my introduction and ended it with, "Let's hear it for JO-DEE!" And as I heard that, I ran out on stage as I always did and started talking... and nothing came out of the microphone. Now I needed a lapel mic because I used my hands a lot during my presentation, that was a key part of it. So, I started to laugh. Although I had a really strong voice, for a crowd of eight hundred people I really needed the mic. So I moved to the side of the stage where the technician was and, while he was fixing my microphone, I started chatting to the crowd making full use of my voice projection abilities, saying, "Gosh, isn't this the worst thing that can happen to a speaker? I know you all understand what I mean, because you're all speakers too! Luckily for me, I can laugh at it, which goes to prove what I'm going to talk about here today."

As I said that, the technician said I was good to go and I could hear my voice over the PA system and the audience applauded. I started telling them my story, and how laughter yoga was created, and then went onto the benefits. Then it was time for them to give it a try.

OMG! I will never forget the feeling I had when all eight hundred people stood up and started following me. They were so enthusiastic that I was blown away; the more energy I gave them, the more they gave back and I was flying. Everyone was laughing and clapping and having a wonderful time. I was on cloud nine. Then as I finished, they all gave me a standing ovation. For the rest of that day and the following day I had an amazing time with everyone who had been in the audience. They came up to me and told me how much they loved my talk.

The boss that hired me, to whom I had sent THAT email by mistake, also came to me and said, "I am so glad you wrote that email because you knocked it out of the park. Everybody loved it. You really lifted the energy for the whole conference."

Tony Buzan was being honoured at the gala dinner that night and I was taking care of him as usual. People kept coming up to me and thanking me for my talk and asking for a picture. I asked Tony if he wanted anything and he said, "Tonight is your night, go and enjoy it." We spent the night dancing together and having fun with all the delegates. It really was a good evening.

The buzz continued the next day with everyone laughing when they saw me. Representatives from five big companies had gone up to my boss and asked if they could book me for their corporate events. Suddenly he was very proud of me. Previously I had been more valuable as an events director, but now he saw me shine as a speaker.

When it was time for Jairek Robbins to give his talk, there was a speaker already on before him, which meant they needed to change laptops on stage. Jairek ran on stage and started his talk but for some reason his slides didn't work. He looked at me and to my surprise said to the audience, "Yesterday I saw the energy go through the roof when you did the session with Jo-Dee, let's get her back to warm you up." The crowd started to applaud and I ran on and did a few exercises with the wonderful crowd, who knew exactly what to do, while he fixed his slides. He thanked me and went on with his talk.

It was an amazing feeling to get such a response from a great speaker and a fantastic audience. I gained so much confidence from that event and some wonderful footage.

That all took place just before Ramadan (the month of fasting) when most of Dubai shuts down and then stays quiet for a further two months because of the extreme heat. All the momentum I had built up from my talk just fell flat because of the timing. In addition, the government was changing the rules for events and imposing taxes that nobody understood yet.

We had a couple of last events before Ramadan actually started and one featured David Rendall, author of *The Freak Factor*, at the American University in Dubai (AUD). I handled this event on my own, without my team, because they were preparing for a different event taking place the following day, featuring four speakers in just the one day. I was also supervising that marathon event, but it was David Rendall's talk that I was really excited about because he was new to our company and I had taken a chance by bringing him out. I am so happy that I did, he was fantastic.

As the guests started to arrive, I noticed my boss glaze over and start one of his panic attacks, so I grabbed him and took him through a few rounds of tapping; by this time I knew what his problem was and how to bring him out of it. Within ten minutes he was back again to meet and greet. Apparently, someone connected with whatever trouble he had had before was present at the event, and that had set him off. The event went very well, all the delegates were loving it, and no one had noticed the few hiccups with my boss. Unfortunately, my boss caught sight of the same person again and reacted in the same way. Again, I pulled him into an empty room and used the same tapping strategy, and again he was okay. This just increased the stress level of my day that had already been really high!

The uncertainty surrounding all the new regulations, procedures and taxes was really taking its toll on our company and tension was building for the bosses. Having been the face of the company for just over a year, I had worked myself into the ground. One lesson I learned here was that people will take as much as you are prepared to give, which in my case was a lot. I accept that it was my responsibility, my choice, I could have said no, but I was afraid of failing.

One day, when my bosses and I were in a coffee shop, one of them turned to me and said, "Now that they are changing how we do events, how are you going to be worth all your money?"

Remember, I was always working fifteen to twenty hours a day, I had become his unofficial personal therapist, and I was devoting my life to working for this company. And suddenly, there was doubt that I was worth my money?? This really made me laugh, and I said, "Well, let me take that problem away from you," and I walked out of the coffee shop. Now this was probably not the smartest thing to do because I had nothing to go to, and I didn't have any money. But he was really taking the mickey, don't you agree?

Earlier that year, I had met Michael, my soul mate. He just 'got me' and was fascinated by my character. Although he was shocked by my sudden move to quit my job, he knew I was being taken advantage of and so kind of agreed. He helped me rent my apartment as I continued to pursue my own career as a speaker.

Chapter 11

Life as a Speaker

We don't laugh because we're happy, we are happy because we laugh

William James

There was not much happening during Ramadan, so I spent a lot of time working on my material and getting media attention. The rest of the time I spent with Michael. The one thing that made our relationship so great was the fact that we always had fun and laughed. Michael, an American CFO of a billion-dollar company, was fifty-eight and I was forty-eight, yet we knew how to make the most of each day. One of the first surprise fun dates he took me on was to feed the stingray in the Dubai Mall Aquarium. We were knee-deep in water wearing our very unflattering plastic dungarees that clashed with our clothes. We had our bucket of fish and waited for the stingray to come and suck the fish from our hands. This was the first time I had ever done anything like that, and it was so much fun. We flirted, laughed and giggled like kids in our own little world.

Michael would always find a way to take my breath away. He knew I loved animals, especially cats, and so he found a cat café. Can you imagine what it was like to have the whole place to ourselves with thirty cats surrounding us? I was in heaven and he used to get a kick out of my childlike playfulness that I had embraced through practising laughter yoga. Everything was new and fun for me. I still choose to look at life like that, and he always said it was infectious.

Because it was Ramadan, many places were either closed altogether or were empty, but we would sit and talk for literally hours, going from lunch to dinner in the same restaurant. We were so wrapped up in one another that we didn't notice the time going by. With Michael as my distraction, Ramadan passed very quickly. One night we went to a nightclub that was holding an eighties party. We had arrived early, like eager teenagers, and there was a big table in the corner that had been reserved. We asked if we could sit there until the guests who had booked it arrived, and the bouncer said we could as long as we left by 1am.

What a night, we danced in our private box with nobody around us and sat playing a game to see who could guess the song title first. As it was eighties night and I was an ex-dancer, used to recognising music from the first few beats, I won. YAY!! It was so wonderful to be sharing this time with Michael and, as usual, we were totally intertwined, unaware of anything around us. He was always dressed well in his designer suits and matching watches, cufflinks, tie-pin, the works. Actually, when he was at work, he would even have his designer Monte Blanc pens. Coincidentally, we were also matching one another on this particular occasion, both wearing a similar shade of purple, completely unplanned.

As we were leaving, a lady came up to us and said, "You

two are so adorable, I couldn't stop watching you all night, what a lovely couple." We laughed, said thank you and left hand in hand, happy and in love. There is something so special about being able to laugh together.

I started having some health issues again after a few months of us being together. I was in perimenopause and without revealing too many details seemed to have my period nonstop for ages. He would just laugh and say, "Well, buying tampons is just a fixture in our dates these days!"

This made me see that what had been missing from so many of my other relationships was laughter. He would love to hear what I had done during the day and was so encouraging. As luck would have it, I was booked for a gig in Pakistan for ICAP (Institute of Chartered Accountants of Pakistan) where I would face my biggest audiences so far, two events each for one thousand CFOs (Chief Financial Officers) and a workshop for thirty VIPs.

Now CFOs are a different breed, and I just so happened to have one at hand to test my content on. Michael gave me great tips: "We like to see details, graphs, pie charts and facts," knowing that I was not too keen on details myself. He told me that I needed to speak their language if I wanted to get their attention. I remember thinking that I only had forty minutes to tell them my story, give them the details of Laughter Yoga and its benefits, and still include at least twenty-five minutes of actual laughter. How was I going to incorporate the details he suggested in such a short space of time?

It took a couple of hours of thinking about how I was going to tackle this challenge before I finally came up with the idea. I knew that there was a lot of research written on the benefits of laughter. There were graphs and pie charts available too! I made a few slides of pie charts, graphs and statistics, about nine slides in all, and then finished with a photograph of a stack of files on a desk with the caption, '300+ research papers on the benefits of laughter'.

I showed him what I planned to do. After asking, "How many of you are CFOs?" knowing full well their hands would all go up, I would simply quickly click through the slides I had prepared saying, "I know that you need to see pie charts (click), graphs (click), statistics (click)…" and when I reached the final slide I would add, "and there are over three hundred research papers on the benefits of laughter, details of which I would be happy to send to you, but for now I just ask you to take my word for it and give it a go."

Michael loved it, he said it showed that I understood my audience and was not only able to give them what they wanted, but also to make a joke out of it, which they would appreciate.

I remember arriving in Karachi, Pakistan and being taken to my five-star hotel. The contract stated that I would get my money in cash, up front. This was to be my first four-figure payment for a gig. I remember getting the dollars and lying on my bed with it all over me! I had finally reached the goal of earning what other speakers were earning. YAY!!

The next day I was in my element as I walked into the huge conference room. It took my breath away, it was possibly the most beautiful I have ever seen. A giant photograph of me was on the wall as the main keynote speaker. The feeling of accomplishment was adding to the excitement. My heart started pounding as the room began to fill; apparently there were more than a thousand delegates. My name was called, and I did my usual run onto the stage. The joke for the CFOs went down a treat and the room was laughing with me as easily as any other talk I had given.

Afterwards, someone came up to me and said he had never seen his boss laugh so much in the fifteen years that he had been working with him. Another came and asked if I could train him to do it, and people were asking to have their picture taken with me, the 'Laughter Lady'.

The next day was also great, it was more intimate, and I was able to go into more detail because I had three hours instead of just forty-five minutes. I actually have a picture of when the VIPs arrived and when they left – what a difference. They were able to share worries they had and ask me for help with different aspects of their lives.

The feedback was so good that the President of ICAP came to me as we were flying to Islamabad for the following day's event and said, "Take as long as you like tomorrow, the audience need more of you." This was great for my confidence and I was so grateful for the opportunity to work with this amazing organisation.

Returning to Dubai on my 'speaker's high', as Michael would call it, meant I was bouncing around and being even more hyperactive than usual. He was so proud of me for achieving what I had set out to do.

Chapter 12

Life as a Speaker (Part 2)

Laughter connects you with people. It's almost impossible to maintain any kind of distance or any sense of social hierarchy when you're just howling with laughter. Laughter is a force for democracy

John Cleese

Not long after my speaking engagements in Pakistan, I was booked to do a two-day workshop for a YPO (Young Presidents' Organization) group. This was a new challenge, just me and a group of eight CEOs who would meet in Portugal, and I embraced it. I was delighted when I arrived at my five-star hotel in Lisbon. Owned by Ronaldo, it was a really trendy hotel; actually it had me laughing within minutes because I couldn't work out how to turn on the lights! Now really, I had spent my whole life in hotels, how hard could it be?! There was not much time for me to figure anything out as I had been invited for dinner with the group and we were setting off soon after I arrived. The eight members of the group were from Morocco, seven male, one female. They were a mixture of CEOs and owners of pharmaceutical, oil, finance, exchange and water companies, etc., you name it. Now this was another level that I had not really interacted so closely with before. They had money to spend and were on a mission to enjoy their freedom.

We went to a very upmarket food court that had live music in the middle and different stalls of restaurants all the way round; I am talking fancy seafood and lots of places to buy alcohol. It was very festive and packed with people. This was my first glimpse of the people I would be spending the next two days with. They were party animals and luckily for me they were paying for all my food and drinks, so I joined in. We started with champagne and carried on from there. They would order a full table of food to share, it was amazing. We had so much fun. Fortunately, I speak French, so I could understand them, and they were happy that I could follow without needing a translator. I was careful to pace myself as I knew I had to keep them focused for two full days, and that was certainly going to be a task!

We met at breakfast and went to the special suite that had been booked for our workshop. It was very comfortable with all kinds of snacks, fruit and drinks provided. Working with a small crowd of CEOs seemed more daunting somehow than addressing the thousands that I had recently. I got started and very soon had them laughing and on the whole they were great; of course, there is always one that will challenge you, but luckily for me I knew my topic inside out, so I could answer easily. He seemed to want to catch me out but wasn't able to!

I managed to get the basics done and taught them the foundation exercises before we had lunch, which turned out to be a good thing. They had decided that they wanted to go into town for lunch. After all, they were in a new city and wanted to explore and be free. Each one of them in their individual careers had a tough schedule and needed to battle to create a home/work balance with their families.

As soon as we sat down for lunch, they started ordering wine. Now, alcohol is a no-no for laughter yoga because it alters many people's judgement, so it's a rule we have that it should be served *after* our sessions. But there was no way I was going to control this group and stop them drinking! So I let them enjoy their lunch and then it was time to go back to cover the afternoon session that I had planned. I made a spur-of-the-moment decision to do it while we walked around town, so we laughed and discussed certain problems that they wanted help with. It was informal but worked well under those circumstances. We had ice creams and laughed and played like kids on a school trip.

I think they really appreciated that because at dinner that night they said how much they had enjoyed our session and how they liked me being so flexible and able to adapt. The next day I knew what to expect, so, when they came in after breakfast, I made a deal with them, suggesting that we did a chunk in the morning without any breaks, went for lunch at 2pm and then had fun again in the afternoon. They were really happy with that plan and paid attention in the morning. Actually, they showed me what executives needed to focus on, so it was a great lesson for me too. These lovely people didn't have financial troubles, so we didn't have to do the 'no money' laughter exercise, but they *were* dealing with millions of dollars at a time and many had to make risky business decisions, so we adapted the exercise to fit them; it was great fun.

One big thing I noticed that was so useful to them was how to deal with their families. After spending all day in control of their big companies, being pushed and pulled in all directions and having to make important decisions, when they got home, exhausted, wanting only to relax, they felt they had to meet the demands of their significant other and kids who were also pushing and pulling them in all directions because they had missed them. I showed them that it was quality, not quantity, of attention that was needed. I suggested that they laughed and played with their family as soon as they got home to make it memorable for them. This would help them to energise and relax, and their kids and partners would receive the attention they so craved.

I showed them a few games and activities, and they were very grateful because they hadn't realised it could be so simple. I had learned this with my own kids: I only got to see them for a very short time, so I needed to create happy memories within the tight timeframe that I had with them.

Well, it seems that I was a hit because they called my agent after a fortnight and booked me for their AGM in Morocco scheduled for a few months later. The many lessons I learned during that trip also gave me confidence to include more management and executive gigs in the future.

Chapter 13

Life as a Speaker (Part 3)

I have not seen anyone dying of laughter, but I know millions who are dying because they are not laughing

Dr Madan Kataria

My speaking jobs were all very different, and one that really left its mark on me was for a cancer charity, Breast Friends. I arrived at the venue a little early as always, I liked to be there to settle in before the audience arrived. The rooms were always different, and this gave me a chance to familiarise myself with it and make any changes if necessary.

I also like to network with the audience beforehand and connect with a few of them before I actually get up on stage. The banners with my larger-than-life photo were all around the venue and the people started to trickle in. In my usual bouncy, bubbly manner, I walked in to start chatting to people as they got their teas and coffees and canapés. Suddenly, I was hit by a huge sense of darkness in the room that was sucking the energy out of me; I tend to be very sensitive to people and pick up their vibes easily. I told the organiser that it would be better for me to wait in the room where the talk would actually take place. I usually do a little pump up laughter to get me energised and needed that a little more on this occasion.

The audience started taking their seats and it was time for me to begin. I remember looking at the faces of these lovely cancer sufferers and survivors and my heart just melted. If anyone needed to laugh, it was these ladies. I did my talk and watched some of them well up as I told my story, and then their eyes lit up when I said how I had overcome all my difficulties through laughter. By the end of the session they were all laughing and crying. Laughter is very cathartic; it takes you to a place of 'nothingness' and somehow enables you to deal with built up pain. As that pain is released, people often cry as well, which is also cathartic.

At the end of the session, as I signed off with my usual, "Remember to live life laughingly," I looked at a totally different audience from the one that had walked in. The darkness that I had picked up on had lifted and even for just that one hour those lovely ladies had a break from the fear and pain they were facing every day. One by one they came up to hug me and thank me and told me how they felt.

This has to be one of the most touching sessions I have ever done. A couple of weeks later, one of the ladies messaged me thanking me for the session and telling me that my story of Enriqué and the watermelon had really helped her. She had a four-year-old daughter who was a little difficult, but when the mother laughed at the things she did, she found it really helped. By using laughter, things had turned around in her relationship with her daughter. YAY!! Result. I love it when I get to hear that things I shared have worked. I don't often get that because I am flown into the conferences and then flown out again, rarely communicating subsequently with anyone that saw me speak.

Although my usual target audience is corporate businesses, I do love it when I get to work with charities like Breast Friends. Another talk that stands out was for a group with Parkinson's disease. The session was held in a park in Dubai and was a lovely day out for this group of people. Their carers sat them in a circle and I gave my talk, which has the same essential message each time, but I always research the client so that I can add new information that relates to them specifically. Those suffering with Parkinson's disease have involuntary shaking of particular parts of their body, stiff and inflexible muscles or slow movements, which makes it hard for them to perform traditional exercises. Through laughter they get to 'jiggle their insides' and move in a way that is easier for them. Laughter provides all the benefits of exercise plus an added boost to their immune system and mood through the 'happy cocktail' of dopamine, oxytocin, serotonin and endorphins. It was great to discover that what I had been sharing with successful business people and corporate clients could also benefit people with specific medical problems who were facing different sorts of challenges and I was so grateful for the opportunity to help these people to find a little bit of joy.

A couple of months later, I was given some devastating news. Michael had to go back to the States. He had some personal things to take care of before we could be together, and this broke my heart. Our love was a forbidden love and all I could do was watch him go and hope for the best that he would come back to me one day soon. Funnily enough, on the last day we had together, I was booked for an hour-long radio interview with Dubai Eye radio station about laughter.

I walked in, my usual bubbly self, did the interview and laughed with everyone; we had loads of fun. The presenter was speaking with me afterwards and she said she could understand how people could laugh when everything was okay, but what about when they are having a hard time? I told her that that particular day was one of the saddest days of my life, I was saying goodbye to the love of my life, and yet I was able to laugh on the outside, even though I was crying on the inside.

Now this brings me to something really important. I am not saying that you should just laugh off the big things and that it's easy. Boy, it's not, my accounts of how I felt when Majid and I started to have relationship problems when we were still in Greece, when I left my kids, when I experienced my various physical and mental health breakdowns and when I had to say goodbye to Michael, despite having seen for myself as far back as 1992 the amazing power of laughter and studied the proven benefits, certainly show that! We also do need to feel all our emotions but, when we are in a situation where we shouldn't show it, laughter helps us get through. Laughter doesn't actually cure anything, it just helps you handle it.

Tip: Remember that laughter requires daily practice.

The parting from Michael was a heartbreak that, to be honest, I still haven't got over completely. But having laughed about the good times we had and laughed at having to let him go, I found it a little easier to move forward. As I said previously (Chapter 8), there are many techniques that I use to deal with issues as big as this, tapping and learning to love myself have really helped too.

Chapter 14

Life in the UK

To truly laugh, you must be able to take your pain and play with it

Charlie Chaplin

Heartbroken, feeling totally lost by the love of my life leaving me and with business declining in Dubai, I made the choice to go back to the UK. As I explained at the end of Chapter 3, I was born in South Africa, but my dad was British, so I have a British passport, for which I am really grateful because it has allowed me to travel freely around the world.

Before heading to the UK, I was going to India to attend a Laughter Yoga Teaching course. Firstly, to refresh what I had learned six years earlier in Johannesburg and to visit the Laughter University head office in Bangalore and secondly, just to get away and allow myself ten days without thinking about my personal problems.

It was a good decision; ten days of non-stop laughing with Dr Kataria and twenty other future Laughter Yogis were just what I needed. The course venue was a beautiful *ashram* where many retreats were held. There was something special about being in the middle of nowhere surrounded by nature and laughter. It was on this course that I started a friendship with Rowee who had travelled from the UK. To my astonishment, I was honoured with the 'Global Laughter Ambassadors' award for all the work I had done over the past six years spreading laughter around the world. Being recognised for doing what I loved was a wonderful feeling. After this injection of joy, I made the move to the UK.

I had a friend who lived in London and am so grateful that she allowed me to stay with her for a bit while I tried to find my feet. But, after two months, I needed to move out because she had family coming. It was here that Rowee came to my rescue. She lived in Woking, Surrey, a twenty-minute fast train ride from London. When I arrived at her door, I was a little defeated for several reasons. I was still heartbroken, I had moved to a new country where nobody knew me and for some reason my energy seemed to be a bit low. Well, I was dealing with more than one area of trauma in my life, I suppose. Also, I was moving further away from my kids: it was no longer a two-hour flight to Iran. But I had high hopes for my business.

Rowee had a small spare room in her flat and very soon she said I could stay as long as I liked. What a life saver, she is truly an angel. She was just beginning her laughter journey and I was happy to help her get started, joining her in setting up a laughter club.

For the first time in what seemed like forever I was sort of stable and 'Simply Laughter Worldwide' became an official company. There was now a 'Ltd' on the end! How exciting, this really got me energised and I started working very hard. I did a business plan and managed to get some funding. I had gone through all my savings with the move and although I was well paid for my one-hour talks, my bookings were sporadic, so my fee didn't go very far.

I became registered with a GP, something I had only experienced briefly when I worked in the UK about ten years earlier around the time of Fatimeh's birth. It still felt like a relatively new experience and for someone who had not had insurance nor free health care before it was amazing. It meant that I needed to go for a 'new patient' appointment as my records hadn't been updated in ten years.

I learnt that my blood pressure was very high, and I was sent for blood tests. Then, suddenly, I was called back in to see the GP. The results of my blood tests were not very good, so I was sent to a nephrologist (kidney specialist) and it was there that I was informed just how bad my kidneys actually were. Lol, I had thought I just got ill every now and then because of some problem with them and then they got better – no big deal. How wrong was I?!

Anyway, I was monitored and told to come back after three months. My kidneys were the reason that I was so tired, they said. It was great knowing that there was an explanation for how I felt. I carried on with my new life.

Rowee and I ran laughter sessions for various organisations, as I wanted to be seen. I found these a bit strange because they weren't corporate audiences and the people I was addressing seemed to be a bit older than those I usually had contact with. For some reason, I wasn't the big hit that I was accustomed to being. Was I losing my edge or did the Brits not like to laugh? I wasn't sure.

I joined the Professional Speaking Association (PSA) as a way to learn how to up my game in the speaking industry and also to network with others in the same field. I really felt at home there and loved every meeting we had. It gave me a huge boost and showed me what was possible.

I started marketing myself and contacting people whom I thought would be interested in my talks. I also put my name forward for DisruptHR London, which was an upcoming event, usually taking place every couple of months, that would give me a great opportunity to be seen by those who may want to hire me. Katrina Collier did a wonderful job organising such an amazing event. It was rather challenging for the speakers, though, because we only had five minutes to speak with twenty slides ready in sequence to be played automatically, changing every fifteen seconds. This meant that I had to have my timing down to every breath. Strange how it's easy to speak for between one and three hours, or even one to two days but trying to fit your message into five minutes is not so easy... especially because mine had actual laughter exercises in it. As hard as it was, it was an awesome experience where I met so many amazing people and once again got the response I had received in the Middle East, YAY!!

Katrina and I became friends and I ended up helping her with future events. I would check people in through the door, which got me seen and many of them would comment on how they remembered my talk on that first occasion. I am truly grateful for this friendship and Katrina is a real inspiration. Through the funds that she raises from all her hard work she supports 'Hope for Justice' and 'The Slave-Free Alliance', organisations that aim to end modern-day slavery.

By now I had been in the UK for about six months and, although people were interested in me, I wasn't getting booked. I was flown back to Dubai to do an hour's talk for the Silicon Oasis Government who were happy to pay my flight, hotel accommodation and four-figure fee, yet in the UK people were not biting. I even managed to pick up an extra 'gig' with DHL while I was in Dubai, and that went down a storm, as usual.

I started to worry about the lack of UK bookings, I changed my promotional material, I made a showreel, I was doing whatever I could think of to get work, but it still wasn't happening yet.

So, I decided to host the 'Simply Laughter Online Summit' (SLOS) where I would interview thirty of the top people in the laughter industry and ten business specialists who could give ideas and advice to help with setting up and running a business. I thought this would be a good way to raise my profile and become better known because I already had an audience and I knew the topic inside-out.

Well, this was no easy task! First, I needed to do a course on how to run online summits and as soon as I finished a module, I was putting into practice what I had just learnt. Connecting with people in America, Australia, Canada and across the globe meant I was filming at all hours of the day and night. I found myself working twenty hours out of twenty-four, again! Thank goodness for Rowee, who fed and watered me all the way through. Bless her, I completely took over her lounge, which had now become my filming studio.

I designed the site with a friend of mine and was becoming really good at all the online processes. It took me three months of hard work and then it was launch week. Something went wrong with the automatic sign up and I needed to do it manually. Again, remember people from all around the world were signing up: this meant I hardly slept.

The first day started with a live call and I had already begun to lose my voice from exhaustion and having spoken in too many interviews. It was rather funny that I was croaking away and would often cough. Laughter isn't the best thing for a cough. Laughter helps you exhale more than you inhale, getting rid of all that 'yucky' air that is lying stagnant in your lungs, which often causes you to cough. Overall, that's good for you, but not when you are hosting a live event!

Luckily, I had some amazing friends join me which helped, and I was off to a great start. The feedback was very positive. It was a five-day summit which was free to watch on the day with the opportunity for viewers to upgrade to VIP membership if they wanted to keep the recordings and get extra worksheets and information. Extracts from this summit can be found in APPENDIX 3.

On the fifth day, we were due to end with another 'live' session and by this time I had no voice at all. This made it even more fun, perhaps challenging is a better word, and again some of the laughter greats like Dave Berman, Robert Rivest and my good friend Rohit Bassi helped out.

Rowee had got a bottle of champagne to celebrate and we were both very proud of what I had achieved. This didn't last too long, however, because I had really pushed myself healthwise and my blood test results were going downhill. I was put on some blood pressure tablets and told to cut down my stress. "Oh yes, nice try, doctor," I thought.

I decided to go and visit my kids who had just moved to Istanbul, Turkey. This was great because it meant that I could dress like I usually did and not cover up like I had to in Iran. Covering up wasn't really a problem, but I felt much freer when it wasn't necessary. My kids were growing up fast and were now pretty much self-sufficient. My daughter was eleven and used to take the train to school and back on her own in a foreign country. She didn't speak English or Turkish to start with. She was amazing, managing to pick up Turkish really quickly, evidence, I think, of how resilient my kids are.

Majid had moved so many times in the years since I had left him that the only constant they knew was that there was no constant. It is something I am still not very happy about, but it doesn't seem to have affected them badly. My son, Enriqué, wanted to play volleyball and so joined a Turkish team after attending trials. They liked him so much that they wanted him to sign a five-year contract. Majid and I decided that would not be a good idea because then they would all need to stay in Turkey. I was so proud of him, though, for achieving this level and being offered the contract.

The best thing about my kids being in Istanbul was that they had Wi-Fi at last, YAY!! They could chat to me on WhatsApp, which had not been possible before when they were still in Iran. This meant we got to talk whenever we wanted to and didn't have to go weeks without speaking.

My kids told me that they laughed with their new friends and that helped with the language barrier. They even kept reminding *me* to laugh if ever I let my guard down. It was really funny. One day we were walking around Taskim Square, where there was an amphitheatre, and Fatimeh ran up onto the stage and started to do my laughter session. She had obviously been watching my videos. It was the cutest thing I had ever seen: a mini-me!

I returned to the UK with my usual energy boost from having seen my kids, which made it easier for me to move forward. I had just become President Elect of London PSA (Professional Speaking Association) and had lots to do to make sure our events were the best they could be. I loved mixing with the best of the best and learning from those who were making a difference. I even started MCing. This was challenging because it had nothing really to do with laughter but, somehow, I managed to let it come through in all I did. It was just after celebrating my election to be the next president that I was given the news that I would need to be on dialysis or have a kidney transplant within the next three to five years. This hit me like a ton of bricks.

Now, as you know, I am the 'Laughter Lady' and have always suggested to the people listening to me that they should laugh at whatever is happening to them, so that they can oxygenate their brains to help them come up with a solution more easily. Sometimes it is a real challenge to do that, of course, and, oh boy, that advice was certainly put to the test when I was given that news. Did I laugh? Actually, no, I didn't at first, BUT laughter did follow after a few days as I started to use the tools I had learned and spoken about for so long. The idea that I could also share them with other people who were suffering I saw as a blessing and it was a comfort to me. People had said that I was the most positive renal patient they had seen; now it was time for me to share my journey and support others. There are millions of people who suffer from some kind of Chronic Kidney Disease (CKD) like me and this was my time to shine.

But there were certainly challenges ahead, with one of the biggest unexpected tests I could have imagined having to face being on the horizon – homelessness.

Anyway, once I did manage to respond with laughter, it certainly helped me enormously to get through the initial shock of my diagnosis and then enabled me to find the positives in my situation.

Getting through the initial shock:

I believe that being able to feel the joy and the sadness of everything that happens is very important and I think the best thing to do when you experience an emotion is to accept it, understand it and yourself and then process it. For many years, before laughter had become part of my everyday life, I just buried my emotions and hid them from others but, seriously, there's only so much a human being can take before they will overflow with unprocessed baggage. Laughter has helped me deal with all my various emotions, control my moods more easily and remain true to my inner feelings.

I may mope a bit in the beginning, cry, get angry, but then let it go. When I eventually laugh at whatever it is that is causing the pain, it usually dispels the negativity and releases it. My thought process goes like this: I have this problem – as a result I feel like this BUT I will laugh, let it go and believe that I'll get through it.

Tip: Acknowledge all your emotions but be ready to let them go. Laughter can set you free.

Looking for the positives

While laughing at the problem, your mind opens to the possibilities of how you can change the situation or get over it. It also becomes easier to find the positives in your situation. In my case, for example, this is what I came up with:

Yes, I have had this terrible news and yet, wow, I am so blessed to have these good things:

1. I am in a country where I have great medical care and support.
2. Because it is a rare disease, I have volunteered to be a research subject to help others.
3. I will finally have a base and settle in the UK (something I have never done before, anywhere).
4. I have family and friends who support me – several friends and my half-sister have offered me one of their kidneys if we are a match (WOW!! That is true caring…).
5. I am a motivational speaker and so I can use my voice to inspire others to find their way to a more positive outcome. I can help spread awareness of this disease (Polycystic Kidney Disease, known as PKD) and also depression.

6. After the transplant I can live a fairly normal life, having been given a second chance.
7. I am lucky I created a job that doesn't follow a normal 9 – 5 office routine, so I am free to undergo treatment and continue to do what I am passionate about.
8. And the list goes on… YAY!!

Tip: No matter how small or big the victory, remember to celebrate life with laughter and say, "Very good, Very good, YAY!!" Let this become second nature.

The last gig I did was a two-day MCing job at the Human Playing Conference (2018) where I got to share the stage with Dr Robert Holden and Patch Adams himself. It was a great event organised by UK Laughter Yoga Master Trainer Lotte Mikkelsen with a whole host of amazing speakers.

It was such fun to watch my heroes on stage and to spend time with them. I had researched their work for years and now there I was rubbing shoulders with them. By the time it came for me to do my talk at the end of the second day, I was exhausted and hardly knew what I was saying! I hoped the message had got through and was relieved that the feedback was good. But I knew I was not well.

Chapter 15

Life with PKD

Laughter is the best way to make somebody's heart beat

Robert Holden

My medication was increased, and I seemed to turn into a zombie. I went from a bubbly, smiley person to someone who suffered from extreme headaches and had absolutely no energy. My body was giving out and would become swollen whenever I walked more than a few steps, making it hard for me to get around. I started to withdraw from everyone and would just hibernate. I found myself in the all-too-familiar downward spiral as I went into a depression. My specialist told me that this was normal for a few reasons. My body was not functioning as it should anymore and by this time my kidney function was only about 25%. From then on it declined 1% every two months on average. I was lacking in iron and therefore anaemic, had hypertension with my blood pressure reaching 180/130 and I also had vitamin D deficiency, common in kidney disease patients. Vitamin D plays an important role in maintaining normal blood levels of calcium and phosphorous, helps promote calcium absorption and regulates parathyroid function.

Brain function is affected by abnormal calcium levels and hyperparathyroidism resulting from vitamin D deficiency causes both chronic fatigue and depression, which are common side effects of kidney failure and especially in my case where there is simply no cure. PKD is a hereditary disease caused by a gene mutation, resulting in many cysts covering the entire kidney, which obviously hinders kidney function. Remember when I told you about the hole in my knee that brought my dancing career to an early end and how I thought my parents must have been blowing bubbles when they made me? Well, there were lots more bubbles in my kidneys... Imagine many little balloons tied tightly together and that is what my kidneys looked like, but not such fun.

Unfortunately, my brother has PKD too, although he is still in stage one, so he can make life changes to inhibit the growth of the cysts. I hope that by the time he reaches stage five like me, there will have been some advancements in the treatment. I am also faced with the 50% chance that my kids will have inherited it from me. One of the positives (always look for a victory, remember!) of me being diagnosed first, was that my brother was tested before he had any symptoms, which has given him time to change his diet and learn from my mistakes.

My journey has been different because I was always travelling and never had a regular GP to monitor my health. I used to take loads of non-steroidal anti-inflammatory drugs (NSAIDs), which are medicines widely used to relieve pain, reduce inflammation and bring down a high temperature. They're often used to treat headaches, painful periods, sprains and strains, colds and flu, arthritis, and other causes of long-term pain. I now know that long-term use of these is not recommended, and side effects can include kidney damage/disease. As a dancer, I was always self-medicating by taking NSAIDs and, when I was in Macau, Iran and Dubai, I also took restricted antibiotics and medication, which were freely available over the counter without a prescription.

Tip: Please don't take meds if they are not prescribed — it's really not a good idea, believe me!

Anyway, after spending a few long months in a downward spiral, there was some good news, Rowee was going to get married, YAY!! I was so happy that she had finally met such a lovely man to spend her life with. This also meant that I needed to move out.

STRESSSSS! I hadn't worked in a while, nor could I in my condition, and I had no money saved. I didn't have a very good credit rating because I had not had a bank account long enough. What was I going to do?

Lost and confused, I went to Woking Council housing department to ask them about my options. The feeling of being this down-and-out was something really scary. I had a ray of hope when they said they could help me, but first I needed to be homeless. Then it hit me, that is exactly what I was. The procedure was that they could only help me once I was there with my bags, and they would not be able to arrange any accommodation in advance of me presenting myself. I told them about my health problems and that I spent most of the evening going to the loo, so having one close to hand would really help.

Back at Rowee's, packing up my few belongings (for years I had travelled around the world with all my possessions fitting into two suitcases), I wondered about where I might end up; was it going to be a shared room with bunk beds, if so, who would I be sharing with and would it be clean? Oh my gosh, all kinds of horror stories were going through my head. The fear of the unknown loves to play games with your mind, but I was happy, at least, that I was not going to be on the street.

Tip: Always look for the positive, something to be grateful for, however bad the situation appears.

I went back to the housing department with a suitcase in each hand a few days later, as arranged, and told them I was officially homeless. My eyes filled with tears of gratitude when they said they had an en-suite room for me, in Woking, and I could go there right away. Although the normal procedure is not to arrange anything in advance, the supervisor said that she had overheard my story a few days earlier and, because of my illness, wanted to do everything in her power to avoid adding to my suffering. As luck would have it, a room had become available the day before I had arranged to go back, and they had kindly held it for me.

Walking into 'The Lodge' and seeing my lovely room gave me so much hope. It was bigger than my room at Rowee's with a bathroom, fridge and cupboards; it even had a nice pink and black duvet. Everything was clean and bright, and I sat on the bed with a huge sigh of relief. Now I had to start from scratch again, but somehow, this time, it was different. I felt that each journey I had been on had taught me something and this would be a fresh beginning using that wisdom. I had always thought that I was grateful for everything, but on that first day when I stepped into The Lodge, I realised what true gratitude felt like. I began to make a list of what I was grateful for every day and was amazed that when I started looking, there were so many things to be grateful for. That kind of works in reverse too, of course, looking for negatives reveals negatives. I even started a gratitude jar. I used to write three things I was grateful for and put them in the jar every day.

> Tip: Keep your own gratitude jar. On the days that you feel down, open the jar and be reminded of what you have. It's a powerful lesson and a great way to lift your spirits.

These days I no longer have a gratitude jar but, before I go to bed, I always remember to list what I am grateful for; my bed, my home, my food, my kids, my friends, my cat, my health, the doctors and nurses, those who support me… and then that is how I fall asleep.

It had already been two years since I said goodbye to Michael, and I decided that I needed to move on from waiting for him. We were still in contact, but nothing was moving forward, and I needed to cut the ties for my own mental well-being. It was time to try my hand at online dating. Oh boy, what had I let myself in for?! Swiping left, swiping right, trying to decide based on a picture and a profile. Endless chatting and crappy dates – why is it that people are so different in person from their profile and chats? When I started my journey into the abyss of online dating, I had thought it would help my depression, but actually it kind of made things worse.

Then, after about three months, a new site popped up catering for over-fifties. I thought this would be better for me, so I set up my profile for one final try before giving up. I 'liked' a few profiles of people nearby whom I thought were suitable and then forgot about it for a couple of days.

About two weeks before I was due to move out of Rowee's flat, a notification came from a man who was an IT Executive. We started chatting and he seemed nice. We agreed to go on a date. He came to pick me up in his fancy BMW, was well-dressed and well-spoken. A car doesn't make the man, I have always thought, but this time he was a BMW of a man, top of the range. He was lovely and a real gentleman. We laughed and joked and had a good time.

When he dropped me home, he got out of the car to open the door and asked to see me again. Wow, a second date! This was such a strange time in my life. I was soon to be homeless and I meet this lovely man who was an executive. I told him I was having a bit of a tough time, but not just how bad it was, well, not in the beginning anyway.

Once I was living at The Lodge, he came to pick me up there too, unaware that it was temporary bed and breakfast accommodation specifically for the homeless; all he knew was that I was not allowed visitors. That was okay with him, as he had a house about twenty minutes away. He would cook me dinner and we would enjoy an evening watching a movie and chatting. He had just come out of a painful breakup with a lady he had spent ten years with, and I was just getting over Michael. We kind of needed each other and supported one another through the hurdles we were facing. It was nice to have someone there for me.

Life at The Lodge was interesting. There were many people with colourful histories staying there, all having experienced some kind of hardship. Some were in hiding because of domestic violence, some were fragile and had just come off suicide watch, some were recently out of prison after repeat offending and many had varying degrees of mental health issues. We all had one thing in common and that was that we were down on our luck.

Now that I had got rid of the stress of having nowhere to live, I decided to take a good look at my life and to stop all the things that were causing me unnecessary stress. I had a habit of volunteering to help and needed to learn how to say no. As a conditioned people helper, it was hard for me to suddenly sit back and say, "Hey, *I* need help." I had always been so strong, but I had gone through so much that it had finally worn me down.

Slowly, one by one, I started cancelling all the things I had planned to do for the next few months. The hardest thing to do was to turn down being the President of London PSA. The people were amazing and so supportive, and I loved every meeting. But it was just too much for the moment.

Jon Baker, the President who had nominated me to take over from him, gave me an amazing send off. We had made a great team, but it was clear I was not as sharp as I used to be, and I was finding it harder and harder to get through the full day. With a brain of mush, my MCing was not very good and I tore myself up about it, because I liked to be the best I could be and, clearly, I was not. It would take me about three days to recover and be able to get out of bed after each monthly meeting. The day was scheduled from 10am – 6pm, but I had to leave the house at 7am to get there in good time and then there were important networking opportunities over drinks afterwards, so I didn't arrive back home until late. I carried on for as long as I could, even when I was at The Lodge, and didn't let too many people know what I was going through. When I left, I just mentioned my health had taken a turn for the worse and that's why I needed to stop.

There were three guys at The Lodge that I got to know and started to hang out with; somehow, we always had a laugh together. One of them, an ex-con called Dave, suggested that we go and visit The Lighthouse, a place where he was helping out. He was very excited about it and said we would be welcome to go and have coffee there. I had often walked past the building, wondering what went on there, but had never ventured inside.

We all decided to support Dave and go along; apparently, on that day we would even get a free lunch. The Lighthouse was a big white building and inside it was furnished like a home. There were armchairs, sofas and tables, a huge open kitchen and a foodbank section in one corner. There were flasks of hot water with a choice of coffee and a selection of teas. Next to that was a big assortment of biscuits and pastries. All free of charge – YAY!!

We were welcomed as we walked in and asked for Dave, although he was pretty easy to find being 6' 2" tall, rather overweight and usually heard chatting away somewhere.

One of the team took me around and showed me what was upstairs, explaining that The Lighthouse is a community space hosting a range of creative projects to support, encourage, and empower those who find themselves on the margins. There was an art section, with all kinds of paints, pens and papers and 'stuff' to use to create art. Then there was a lovely comfortable and inviting room used for a programme called Nurture. And on the far end of this huge floor was an area labelled 'Esteem Ahead' full of all different clothes hanging on rails.

There was also a little coffee shop called 'The Cozy' that served amazing coffee, sandwiches, light snacks and cakes; the profits generated from that fund The Lighthouse, along with donations.

The guys and I sat around for the community lunch, which was for anyone who needed a meal and was down on their luck. I had gone from five-star hotels to this; it was a lot to get my head around at first. There were about twenty people sitting round the table, a mixture of rough sleepers (homeless and living on the street), vulnerable people, those struggling on a low income and people suffering with various mental health issues. At first it was a little daunting because I had not been out much and had become a bit of a recluse (a side effect of being depressed), but here there was loads of laughing and chatting and people were having fun. I felt safe because I was with my mates from The Lodge. We tended to look out for one another.

This soon became our regular hangout on a Monday, Wednesday, Thursday and Friday. At 'Esteem Ahead' they styled and colour-coded me, giving me five carefully-selected outfits that I could take home. What?! This was amazing, I felt great. The helpers there said that that was the idea, "We want people to look good so that they feel good." They had clothing suitable to wear for interviews and for taking the first steps in rebuilding lives.

I soon got to meet the person behind The Lighthouse; her name is Rebecca (Bex to me). Oh boy, she is an angelic lady who just oozes love. Not only is she beautiful, but she has this great way of making people feel safe and supported. This was something I desperately needed too but was still a little shy about admitting. We sat and had a coffee and chatted and I opened up a bit about what I had been going through and told her I was a speaker on laughter. Of course, this set her off and she was very interested in what I did. She said that she would love me to share some laughter with her and her family, when I was ready, but I was there to receive not give.

For me, the greatest thing about Bex and The Lighthouse is that it is run by Christians, but anyone is welcome, and there is no Bible pushing going on. As Bex says, she believes in showing God's love in action rather than by just speaking about it. And boy, did I feel this.

I was invited to the weekly Nurture group held on Monday mornings and I also signed up for the 'Baking Table'. Hehe, I wanted to do something I wouldn't usually do, and that was cooking, without a doubt! Instead of trying to make money or finding a client to 'fix', for once my priority was myself. It was time to be kind to myself and find out a bit more about who I was.

The first group session I went to was the 'Baking Table'; there were about six people there and I was welcomed and shown where to get my apron. Then it was time to make bread. Oh my gosh! Who would have thought that making bread could be so cathartic? We took hold of the dough then followed the instructions, "Pull up, punch, punch, turn and repeat." It was not easy and certainly worked up a sweat. We chatted in our small group as we kneaded the bread. I was laughing, of course, and making everyone else laugh. It never takes long for that to happen because I just laugh at anything anyway.

At the end of the session I walked away very proud of the eight twisted bread rolls I had made. It was the very first time I had attempted to make bread. I was really happy with my results and went back home and slept. Napping was my new go-to. I couldn't do anything without needing a nap afterwards, so after all that kneading I definitely needed one!

On the following Monday, I was excited about going to the Nurture group. We were each given notebooks, then started with some breathing exercises and light stretching, followed by a few minutes of mindfulness and meditation. For the last forty-five minutes, there was a speaker on nutrition; in subsequent sessions, the topics covered included stress, goal setting, finding your strengths, clothing, makeup, etc., basically anything that was needed in order to nurture yourself.

It was a place for discussion and healing, which was encouraged by the very homely feel of the décor. There was no pressure to share if it was too difficult, and I felt at ease with a lovely group of girls. I did go on to share laughter with them after about a month or so, once I started to feel a bit more human.

By this time, out of the four of us that had started to hang out together at The Lodge, I had become particularly good friends with Tony, and we made sure to look out for one another. It was thanks to him that I got up every morning and went into town or to The Lighthouse; without him knocking on my door it would have been so easy just to stay in bed all day.

Everyone who came to The Lighthouse now knew me because I was such a regular and I also helped out a lot. Of course – I always have to be a part of it all! In fact, several people mistook me for a member of staff rather than a service user! One of my favourite people who came into The Lighthouse was a man who used to laugh his head off for no reason. You could hear him from anywhere in the building and he just couldn't stop, he was amazing. He would even give me a run for my money.

The more time I spent at The Lighthouse, the more my laughter came back naturally. I had not been doing my daily practice session for a while and had half-forgotten those wise words, "You don't laugh because you're happy, you're happy because you laugh," that I had first heard from Dr Kataria. It was time to get back to basics and get myself back on track.

After a couple of months at The Lodge, I was offered a lovely one-bedroom apartment on the canal. Somehow, unlike many in The Lodge, my paperwork all ran smoothly, and the council moved me in and helped me with all the deposits and rent. They were very happy and said I was a model case and a perfect tenant. Everyone was happy. Of course, I was so grateful.

It was the first time I had moved into an apartment on my own, and 80% of my stress was removed by feeling settled and secure. This was the perfect place for me to get well. My new life had begun.

I continued to see Graham, the lovely IT Executive with the BMW, for about four months, but for some strange reason he didn't want a long-term relationship with me; I mean, really! How could he not want me? Lol, I was perfect for him. I was a little upset because he was the first man that had actually got my mind off Michael. Graham and I had a strange bond and kept in touch, nonetheless. After a few months, we got talking again and he decided to help me with a project I was working on.

Being me, I can't just be depressed and leave it at that, I need to analyse why and find a way to help myself and others. I had been working with another IT specialist to develop an app that could read emotions and translate them into data, which would allow me to prove quantitatively just how much laughter helped. My plan was to build an app that would help people realise when they were heading towards a downward spiral before getting into a full-blown depression. This has a key application for people working in corporations with high stress jobs. Depression and stress-related illnesses cost companies a fortune.

This project had been on and off for a couple of years because of my health and living situation, but now I could focus on it. With Graham being an IT man and really caring for me, I trusted him. This led us to start working together. Now we were business partners. Lol, I had wanted him as a life partner, and I got even more.

Graham is someone I am grateful to call a true friend and has been key in my ongoing recovery. He is always there to give me a slap if I need it or a hand up if I am a bit down. We have both been through so much in the past eighteen months together that I couldn't imagine my life without him. Yes, you've guessed it, he's one and the same Graham who kindly takes me to my various appointments and entertains the nurses and other medical staff with me.

Tip: Surround yourself with good, positive people. People who will light your fire, not put it out. People who make you think and cover all areas, not just "Yes" people, those who have your back.

As my condition worsened, I joined groups to find out as much as I could about kidney disease, transplants, dialysis and anything else that could help me. One thing I noticed with most groups was just how much people were suffering and not being understood. Having an invisible illness leads to a lot of stress.

Take me, for example, it's always been my character to be bubbly and happy; these days, I am a slightly toned-down version of that, but it's still there. I don't complain and most people don't know just how sick I am. Even my doctors have said I don't look as sick as my results show that I am. It's my show face. I'm the happiest renal patient they've ever seen.

There is a story by Christine Miserandino called The Spoon Theory (See Appendix 3), which I think really explains very well what it's like to live with a debilitating disease or condition. It seems to be a simple and quick way for my friends and people I meet to begin to understand the challenges I face with daily life.

Although it's very hard for those of us living with

a chronic illness, we don't have to let it win. Our illness does not define us. We can choose to hit back with positive actions. It's a choice between giving up or changing the way we think. I know I chose the second. Sure, I have down days, oh boy, I do and that is okay. I throw myself a real pity party. It is important to give each emotion its time, work through it, understand it and then let it go. It is okay to be sad, and angry about having to deal with everything that comes with our condition; it doesn't seem fair, but once I've experienced those feelings, I don't want to stay in that mindset. Visit it, just don't buy real estate there and move in!

By taking control of your emotions and knowing you can change them, you can change your mood and be positive overall. You have many things to be grateful for, just remember to look for them and you might even see an improvement in your outlook.

Tip: If something negative happens, try to laugh and brush it off at least a little and see how you feel afterwards. Watch funny films rather than the news, that's a sure way to bring you down. Look for opportunities to be nice, pay compliments and notice the good. I bet if you try it for a couple of days you will see the difference.

Chapter 16

Life on Dialysis

When you realise how perfect everything is you
will tilt your head back and laugh at the sky
                                                    Buddha

At the moment I am waiting to have a kidney transplant. I am very grateful that a few friends came forward and offered to donate a kidney but, unfortunately, this wasn't possible because of blood type differences or other complications. That was really traumatic, receiving offers of a kidney and then not being able to proceed. Gosh I felt it, a transplant is the way forward for me to have a chance to live a normal life.

Luckily enough, my half-sister Susie, in South Africa, was one of the people who came forward and her blood group is B+ like me, YAY!! Yes, I had to be 'Be Positive', didn't I?! It's what I stand for with every cell of my being, hehe, now I know why. Susie started having all the blood tests and x-rays needed to be allowed to donate. It is a rather complicated procedure. Then, shortly after my fifty-first birthday in February 2020, we got the okay for her to come to the UK to do the tissue typing and last tests before we would go ahead with the transplant. It was to take about four to six months… But, of course, COVID-19 put all those plans on hold. All live transplants were cancelled for the first four months and then only transplants involving UK donors were allowed to take place. This meant that I was added to the waiting list and, as if that wasn't enough of a blow, I was told that I am difficult to match because I have 80% antibodies. Apparently, this arose from all the trouble I had when my daughter was born. All those bits of placenta left behind caused my body to mount an immune response and my high antibody level is the result of that. Not really a good situation to be in when you are about to receive a 'foreign' kidney. I would need to be put on the highest amount of anti-rejection meds, which then raises other issues. Wow, the price of life, eh?

I have recently (August 2020) started dialysis while I wait for a kidney. As well as being on the list, I have Susie waiting for the COVID-19 travel bans to be lifted to see if we can move forward. Back at the beginning of this book, I described having the peritoneal catheter put in ready to start dialysis when the renal team thought it was appropriate. Soon afterwards, one of my friends phoned to check on my progress and asked how my 'tentacle' was doing. How we laughed! Shortly afterwards, I decided to call him 'Timmy, the tentacle' – it sounds more affectionate asking, "How's Timmy?" instead of "How is your catheter?" and, after all, I am rather fond of him, he's keeping me alive… You could even say that I'm very attached to him, lol.

On a positive note, Majid is hoping to move to the UK, which means I will be able to see my kids easily and Enriqué may have another opportunity to play volleyball at a high level. Even though Majid and I have had our really tough times, I am forever grateful to him. He has done a great job of raising my babies and I have learnt many lessons along the way. I would not have changed this journey for anything, it's made me who I am and given me two perfect kids.

Now that WhatsApp is available in Iran, I get to spend a lot of time with them. They video call me and we laugh and have fun. It's not like being with them in person, but it's the next best thing.

I hope that you found some tips in my story to help you stay positive. Tips that show how to get over the difficult times and how to celebrate the good times. Hopefully you are saying "YAY!!" much more often. In the appendices I have included a few pages on the health benefits of laughter and benefits of laughter at work. So, wherever you are:

"Remember to live life laughingly." Because Laughter is Your Lifeline.

Appendix 1

Benefits of Gibberish Meditation

- Breaks the continual verbalisation pattern in the brain.
- Breaks the idea of possessions and identification with things and people.
- Allows you to let go of all the stored anger, grief and guilt without damaging your relationships.
- Makes you more vocal and confident.
- Makes you more conscious and aware.

Appendix 2

Forgiveness Exercise – Louise Hay

Begin to visualise yourself as a small child of about five or six. Look deeply into this little child's eyes. See the longing that is there and realise that there is only one thing that this little child wants from you and that is love.

So, reach out your arms, and embrace this child, hold it with love and tenderness. Tell it how much you love it, how much you care. Admire everything about this child and say that it's okay to make mistakes while you are learning and promise that you will always be there no matter what. Then let this child get very small until it's just the size to fit into your heart and put it there. So, whenever you look down, you can see this little face looking up at you and you can give it lots of love.

Now visualise your mother, as a little girl of four or five, frightened and looking for love, and not knowing where to find it. Reach out your arms, and hold this little girl, and let her know how much you love her, how much you care. Let her know she can rely on you to always be there, no matter what. And when she quietens down and begins to feel safe, let her get very small, just the size to fit into your heart. Put her there with your own little child and let them give each other lots of love.

Now do the same for your father and anyone else that you may have issues with. Feel love for these people and remember they are only people doing the best they can with what they know.

Appendix 3

The Spoon Theory – Christine Miserandino

www.butyoudontlooksick.com

"My best friend and I were in the diner, talking. As usual, it was very late, and we were eating French fries with gravy. Like normal girls our age, we spent a lot of time in the diner while in college, and most of the time we spent talking about boys, music or trivial things, which seemed very important at the time. We never got serious about anything in particular and spent most of our time laughing.

As I went to take some of my medicine with a snack as I usually did, she watched me with an awkward kind of stare, instead of continuing the conversation. She then asked me out of the blue what it felt like to have Lupus and be sick. I was shocked not only because she asked the random question, but also because I assumed that she knew all there was to know about Lupus. She came to doctors with me, she saw me walk with a cane, and throw up in the bathroom. She had seen me cry in pain, what else was there to know?

I started to ramble on about pills, and aches and pains, but she kept pursuing, and didn't seem satisfied with my answers. I was a little surprised as, being my roommate in college and friend for years, I thought she already knew the medical definition of Lupus. Then she looked at me with a face every sick person knows well, the face of pure curiosity about something no one healthy can truly understand. She asked what it felt like, not physically, but what it felt like to be me, to be sick.

As I tried to gain my composure, I glanced around the table for help or guidance, or at least stall for time to think. I was trying to find the right words. How do I answer a question I never was able to answer for myself? How do I explain every detail of every day being affected, and give the emotions a sick person goes through with clarity? I could have given up, cracked a joke like I usually do, and changed the subject, but I remember thinking if I don't try to explain this, how could I ever expect her to understand? If I can't explain this to my best friend, how could I explain my world to anyone else? I had to at least try.

At that moment, the spoon theory was born. I quickly grabbed every spoon on the table; hell, I grabbed spoons off the other tables. I looked at her in the eyes and said, "Here you go, you have Lupus." She looked at me slightly confused, as anyone would when they are being handed a bouquet of spoons. The cold metal spoons clanked in my hands, as I grouped them together and shoved them into her hands.

I explained that the difference between being sick and being healthy is having to make choices or to consciously think about things when the rest of the world doesn't have to. The healthy have the luxury of a life without choices, a gift most people take for granted.

Most people start the day with an unlimited number

of possibilities, and energy to do whatever they desire, especially young people. For the most part, they do not need to worry about the effects of their actions. So, for my explanation, I used spoons to convey this point. I wanted something for her to actually hold, for me to then take away, since most people who get sick feel a "loss" of a life they once knew. If I was in control of taking away the spoons, then she would know what it feels like to have someone or something else, in this case Lupus, being in control.

She grabbed the spoons with excitement. She didn't understand what I was doing, but she is always up for a good time, so I guess she thought I was cracking a joke of some kind like I usually do when talking about touchy topics. Little did she know how serious I would become.

I asked her to count her spoons. She asked why, and I explained that when you are healthy you expect to have a never-ending supply of "spoons". But when you have to now plan your day, you need to know exactly how many "spoons" you are starting with. It doesn't guarantee that you might not lose some along the way, but at least it helps to know where you are starting. She counted out twelve spoons. She laughed and said she wanted more. I said no, and I knew right away that this little game would work when she looked disappointed and we hadn't even started yet. I've wanted more "spoons" for years and haven't found a way yet to get more, so why should she? I also told her to always be conscious of how many she had, and not to drop them because she can never forget she has Lupus.

I asked her to list off the tasks of her day, including the most simple. As she rattled off daily chores, or just fun things to do, I explained how each one would cost her a spoon. When she jumped right into getting ready for work as her first task of the morning, I cut her off and took away a spoon. I practically jumped down her throat. I said, "No! You don't just get up. You have to crack open your eyes, and then realise you are late. You didn't sleep well the night before. You have to crawl out of bed, and then you have to make yourself something to eat before you can do anything else, because if you don't, you can't take your medicine, and if you don't take your medicine you might as well give up all your spoons for today and tomorrow too." I quickly took away a spoon and she realised she hadn't even got dressed yet.

Showering cost her a spoon, just for washing her hair and shaving her legs. Reaching high and low that early in the morning could actually cost more than one spoon, but I figured I would give her a break; I didn't want to scare her right away. Getting dressed was worth another spoon. I stopped her and broke down every task to show her how every little detail needs to be thought about. You cannot simply just throw clothes on when you are sick. I explained that I have to see what clothes I can physically put on, if my hands hurt that day buttons are out of the question. If I have bruises that day, I need to wear long sleeves, and if I have a fever I need a sweater to stay warm and so on. If my hair is falling out I need to spend more time to look presentable, and then you need to factor in another five minutes for feeling bad that it took you two hours to do all this.

I think she was starting to understand when she theoretically hadn't even got to work and she was left with six spoons. I then explained to her that she needed to choose the rest of her day wisely, since when your "spoons" are gone, they are gone. Sometimes you can borrow against tomorrow's "spoons", but just think how hard tomorrow will be with fewer. I also needed to explain that a person who is sick always lives with the looming thought that tomorrow may be the day that a cold comes, or an infection, or any number of things that could be very dangerous. So, you do not want to run low on "spoons", because you never know when you truly will need them. I didn't want to depress her, but I needed to be realistic, and unfortunately being prepared for the worst is part of a real day for me.

We went through the rest of the day, and she slowly learned that skipping lunch would cost her a spoon, as well as standing on a train, or even typing at her computer too long. She was forced to make choices and think about things differently. Hypothetically, she had to choose not to run errands, so that she could eat dinner that night.

When we got to the end of her pretend day, she said she was hungry. I summarised that she had to eat dinner, but she only had one spoon left. If she cooked, she wouldn't have enough energy to clean the pots. If she went out for dinner, she might be too tired to drive home safely. Then I also explained that what I didn't even bother to add into this game was that she was so nauseous that cooking was probably out of the question anyway. So, she decided to make soup, it was easy. I then said it is only 7pm, you have the rest of the night but maybe end up with one spoon, so you can do something fun, or clean your apartment, or do chores, but you can't do it all.

I rarely see her emotional, so when I saw her upset, I

knew maybe I was getting through to her. I didn't want my friend to be upset, but at the same time I was happy to think finally maybe someone understood me a little bit. She had tears in her eyes and asked quietly, "Christine, how do you do it? Do you really do this every day?" I explained that some days were worse than others; some days I have more spoons than most. But I can never make it go away and I can't forget about it, I always have to think about it. I handed her a spoon I had been holding in reserve. I said simply, "I have learned to live life with an extra spoon in my pocket, in reserve. You need to always be prepared."

It's hard, the hardest thing I ever had to learn is to slow down, and not do everything. I fight this to this day. I hate feeling left out, having to choose to stay home, or to not get things done that I want to. I wanted her to feel that frustration. I wanted her to understand that everything everyone else does comes so easy, but for me it is one hundred little jobs in one. I need to think about the weather, my temperature that day, and the whole day's plans before I can attack any one given thing. When other people can simply do things, I have to attack it and make a plan like I am strategising a war. It is in that lifestyle, the difference between being sick and healthy. It is the beautiful ability to not think and just do. I miss that freedom. I miss never having to count "spoons".

After we were emotional and talked about this for a little while longer, I sensed she was sad. Maybe she finally understood. Maybe she realised that she never could truly and honestly say she understands. But at least now she might not complain so much when I can't go out for dinner some nights, or when I never seem to make it to her house and she always has to drive to mine. I gave her a hug when we walked out of the diner. I had the one spoon in my hand, and I said, "Don't worry. I see this as a blessing. I have been forced to think about everything I do. Do you know how many spoons people waste every day? I don't have room for wasted time, or wasted "spoons" and I chose to spend this time with you."

Ever since this night, I have used the spoon theory to explain my life to many people. In fact, my family and friends refer to spoons all the time. It has been a code word for what I can and cannot do. Once people understand the spoon theory, they seem to understand me better, but I also think they live their life a little differently too. I think it isn't just good for understanding Lupus, but anyone dealing with any disability or illness. Hopefully, they don't take so much for granted or their life in general. I give a piece of myself, in every sense of the word when I do anything. It has become an inside joke. I have become famous for saying to people jokingly that they should feel special when I spend time with them, because they have one of my "spoons"."

© Christine Miserandino

Appendix 4

Health Benefits of Laughter (1 – 9)

1 Who Would Like a Joy Cocktail?

Time for a D.O.S.E. of Happy Chemicals...

Laughter is the fastest way to trick the brain into releasing the following ingredients:

🏆 Dopamine: The Reward hormone, considered the "Feel Good Hormone".
Helps with:
*Exhilaration
*Bliss
*Motivation
*Concentration
*Movement
*Learning

💝 Oxytocin: The Love hormone, known to increase trust.
Helps with:
*Bonding
*Arousal
*Trust

*Communication skills
*Anti-stress
*Self-esteem

☺Serotonin: The Calm hormone, for well-being and happiness.
Helps with:
*Mood
*Sense of well-being
*Appetite
*Sleep
*Memory

Endorphins: Feelings of euphoria and pleasure, e.g.
   'Runners' High'.
Helps with:
*Relieving stress
*Relieving pain
*Feeling of euphoria
*Pleasure

Fifteen minutes of full belly laughter and you will get this cocktail with all these amazing health benefits.

Simple. What are you going to do today that will help you get your DOSE of laughter?

2 Are You Reacting Or Responding to Life?

Event+**R**eaction=**O**utcome (E+R=O) is an equation that can really change your life.

A Reaction is usually negative but learning to laugh can change that into a more positive Response, which will then lead to a better Outcome.

Consider being stuck in traffic during rush hour, for example, and being asked the question, "How is this affecting you today?"

A typical reply, with some irritation, might be, "There is always something that goes wrong on this bridge, we have been here for hours, I am furious because I'm going to be so late."

Alternatively, the reply could be, "I heard about this on the news this morning. I left earlier and made sure I had a flask of coffee and something to nibble on. I also had my favourite podcast ready to listen to, and it is fine."

You see the same Event and two very different answers, the first is a reaction and the second a response.

Laughter helps you change the way you see things. Next time something annoys you try laughing at it and see how you feel. YAY!!

3 Is the Way You Are Breathing Causing You Dis-Ease?

As an asthma sufferer, this is really close to home for me. Laughter Yoga provides an excellent cardiac workout and triggers a breathing pattern that offers significant respiratory benefits. It decreases the amount of residual air in the lungs, replacing it with oxygen-rich air. During laughter you exhale more than you inhale and eliminate that stagnant air that can cause dis-ease.

Laughter Yoga is so called because of the breathing techniques used. Known as pranayama, these techniques date back to the origins of yoga that were introduced in ancient texts.

4 Laughter Will Help Strengthen Your Immune System

Watching a one-hour comedy video, for example, has been found to produce:

- 😁 Increased number and activation of T cells;
- 😁 Increased number of Helper T cells (the cells attacked by the AIDS virus);
- 😁 Increased ratio of Helper/Suppressor T cells;
- 😁 Increased number and activity of Natural Killer (NK) cells;
- 😁 Increased levels of Gamma Interferon;
- 😁 Increased number of B cells.

Right now, in our current situation, it is so important to make sure we are doing everything we can to strengthen our immune system.

Laughter decreases stress hormones and increases immune cells and infection-fighting antibodies, thus improving your resistance to disease.

Laughter Online University explains:

When you laugh, the diaphragm becomes a powerful pump

for your lymphatic circulation, much like your heart serves as the central pump that propels blood through your blood vessels.

This assists the lymphatic vessels in carrying this fluid through your body and helps your lymph nodes to clean and filter this fluid, removing waste products, dead cells, and even unwanted microorganisms.

Maintaining clean body fluids is important because these are necessary for you to be at your best. Increased lymphatic flow = an elevated, improved immune system just by the simple nature of more lymph flowing through the nodes, thus producing more lymphocytes, antibodies, etc.

Now that we are all online, we can have a daily laughter routine. Laughter sessions can be found online.

Make sure you get your daily dose 😁

5 Laughter Is Good for Your Heart

As someone who suffers from hypertension due to my failing kidneys, I find the following benefits really useful.

Six benefits of laughter for better heart health – courtesy of the Providence Health team

When was the last time you laughed from your belly? If you can't remember, it's time to find your funny. Your heart will thank you in the most incredible ways. When you have a good laugh, you can reap the heart-healthy rewards for up to twenty-four hours after your chortles and chuckles have stopped:

Increase blood flow

When you laugh your blood vessels expand, increasing blood flow throughout your body. Having a healthy blood flow means your heart, muscles, arms and legs are getting an optimal flow of oxygen-rich blood, which helps reduce your risk of heart attack and other cardiovascular problems.

Decrease stress hormones

Stress constricts your blood vessels and decreases your circulation. Chronic stress can leave you vulnerable to serious conditions such as heart disease, blood clots and heart attack. Laughter stimulates circulation and helps relax your muscles, both of which help reduce some of the physical symptoms of stress as well as the health risks to your heart. Laughter can lighten burdens, inspire hope and encourage deeper connections. It is also a great way to reduce feelings of anger, a common stress trigger.

Reduce artery inflammation

A good hearty laugh causes the inner lining of your blood vessels to dilate by releasing nitric oxide, a chemical compound that helps reduce inflammation and prevent plaque from forming in your arteries. In fact, laughing may be just as effective at reducing inflammation as engaging in aerobic exercise or taking cholesterol-lowering drugs, known as statins.

Increase "good" cholesterol levels

High LDL cholesterol (the bad kind) can lead to heart disease if it is left untreated. Laughing has shown to positively affect the HDL cholesterol (the good stuff) in your body. Good cholesterol flows through your blood and pushes the bad cholesterol out of your arteries, back to the liver. It is then eliminated. Laugher is particularly important for diabetic patients, who usually have lower HDL cholesterol levels. Diabetics who laugh approximately thirty minutes a day increase their HDL cholesterol about twenty-six percent at the end of twelve consecutive months.

Improve blood vessel function

Laughter may encourage your endothelium, the tissue that forms the inner lining of blood vessels, to expand and increase blood flow. Having a healthy endothelium can help prevent atherosclerosis (a hardening of the blood vessels) and cardiovascular disease.

Reduce your risk of heart disease

Laughter is good for your cardiovascular system because it helps prevent a build-up of fats, cholesterol and other substances in and on your artery walls. Laughing leaves a lasting and positive effect on your blood pressure and relaxes your body. Seeking out positive or humorous experiences can change your physiology and help you stay well.

6 Laughter Is 200% Stronger Than Morphine (Dr Joe Currier)

I have had a few clients who have come to my Laughter Yoga sessions suffering from a variety of immobilising illnesses. Fibromyalgia is one of the lesser known but widespread of these diseases and it's amazing to see the transformation in these people from the beginning to the end of the class.

When they say it's the best way for them to get some relief, I am reminded of Dr Norman Cousins, author of *Anatomy of an Illness*, whose story I first heard from Dr Kataria in 2011 (Chapter 6).

Tip: Never doubt the power of the mind over the body. Next time you are in pain, try laughing and let your neurochemicals help you get through it.

7 Did You Know That Laughter Is An Aerobic Exercise?

Ever laughed so much your stomach ached?

"Hearty laughter is a good way to jog internally without having to go outdoors." (Dr Norman Cousins)

Even the fittest of us don't work out all of our body. Laughter is the only way to jiggle your insides and exercise them.

Many chronically ill patients can have a full-body workout by just laughing.

Here is the science:

Mirthful laughter is associated with short term 'aerobic exercise'-like effects, as evidenced by muscle contractions, sharply fast and sporadic deep breathing (Fry, 1977), increased heart rate and oxygen consumption (Fry et al. 1988).

Controlled studies in healthy students have demonstrated that laughter is associated with significant increases in stroke volume and cardiac output.

There are associated decreases in arterio-venous oxygen difference and total peripheral resistance (Boone et al. 2000).

Laughter also helps motivate the elderly to participate in physical activity and to adhere to exercise programs (Hirosaki et al. 2013).

When was the last time you laughed so hard your belly ached?

8 Laugh Your Way to Better Mental Health (Milder Cases Like Depression and Anxiety)

A chuckle a day keeps the doctor away: therapeutic humour and laughter…

We already know that we can have a "joy cocktail" of dopamine, oxytocin, serotonin and endorphins to change our mood.

Laughter bypasses the sympathetic stress arousal system and stimulates the parasympathetic nervous system.

This simply means laughter helps you stay calm in a stressful situation.

Tip: Don't sweat the small stuff, laugh it off.

Some fun:

Martin (2001) traced one of the earliest notations of laughter's health benefits to a biblical reference, Proverbs 17:22: "a merry heart doeth good like a medicine".

Hassed (2001) noted that, in the 17th century, "The arrival of a good clown exercises more beneficial influence… than that of twenty asses laden with drugs."

In the 18th century, Immanuel Kant, "considered laughter useful for restoring equilibrium."

9 Laugh Yourself to Sleep

A good laugh and a long sleep are the best cures in the doctor's book.

Well, they just might go hand in hand…

Laughter increases the body's production of melatonin (the hormone released by the brain at sleep onset).

Laughter produces endorphins, which can help lower levels of the stress hormones cortisol and adrenaline. Those wonderful endorphins can help relieve pain and relax the nervous system.

Laughter helps relieve stress, so you sleep better.

Laughter is a painkiller, so you sleep better.

Laughter oxygenates all your cells, so you sleep better.

And the list goes on… zzzz

Appendix 5

Benefits of Laughter in Business (1–6)

1 Team Engagement: Teams That Laugh Together Work Well Together

Living in this day and age we are all faced with so much stress every day caused by:

😁 Many different cultures, religions and temperaments cohabiting and working together.
😁 Dealing with the traffic/commuting.
😁 Dealing with budgets and deadlines.
😁 Unproductive teams.
😁 Huge staff turnover.
😁 Keeping up with changing times.

Through laughter you can connect teams and develop their communication skills. There will be fewer misunderstandings and more collaboration.

Businesses that I have run workshops with have come back to me and commented years later about how they still remember what I showed them and use it in meetings. It really is as simple as "Ho, Ha, He".

It's a bit difficult to remain caught up in workplace

drama when you're so tickled by a colleague that you can't keep a straight face.

Now with the current situation of a global pandemic, it is more important than ever to keep them engaged as a team. Luckily online programs are available.

2 Productivity: If You Stop Your Teams Laughing, They Will Be Less Productive!

"Laughter is the sun that drives winter from the human face." (Victor Hugo)

"Laughter relieves stress and boredom, boosts engagement and well-being and spurs not only creativity and collaboration but also analytic precision and productivity." (Alison Wood Brooks, Harvard Business School professor)

+31% Increase in Productivity
+37% Increase in Sales
+44% Higher Staff Retention

☺ Happy people solve problems in a much more constructive way. They do not focus on blaming.

☺ Happy people have more energy and are more motivated. Sure, you've realised this one.

☺ Happy people are more optimistic, and there are studies claiming that optimists are more productive and more successful in their lives.

☺ Happy people learn faster as a result of being more

relaxed and open to new experiences.

☺ Happy people make better decisions because they are not in crisis situations.

Happy to go to work:

When staff laugh and have fun together, they have a good time at work, which is why it is really important to make sure the atmosphere is a happy one. We spend so much of our time at work that it's vital that it is pleasant, and the staff enjoys coming to work. Regular Laughter Yoga/wellness sessions and other creative fun activities can ensure people remain happy to go to work.

Afternoon lull: Many people experience a noticeable dip in their alertness, energy level and ability to concentrate in the afternoon. One great way to combat this is a boost of laughter.

You know I like my science, have a look at the research:

Research case 1

Effect of Workplace Laughter Groups on Personal Efficacy Beliefs
Heidi Beckman Ph.D., Nathan Regier & Judy Young

This study measured the impact of a purposeful aerobic laughter intervention on employees' sense of self-efficacy in the workplace. Participants were thirty-three employees of a behavioural health centre.

They met for fifteen-minute sessions on fifteen consecutive workdays and engaged in a guided program of non-humour dependent laughter. The primary outcome measure was the Capabilities Awareness Profile, a self-report self-efficacy questionnaire.

Employees demonstrated a significant increase in several different aspects of self-efficacy, including self-regulation, optimism, positive emotions and social identification, and they maintained these gains at follow-up.

Purposeful laughter is a realistic, sustainable, and generalisable intervention that enhances employees' morale, resilience and personal efficacy beliefs.

Research case 2

One experiment in 2016 found that employees who had chuckled at a comedy video clip were 10% more productive than co-workers who hadn't.

Productivity, in this case, was measured by the number of additional problems they could correctly solve in ten minutes in a lab setting. "The broad message from the literature on the link between happiness and productivity is that both positive and negative emotions have a potentially powerful economic effect," University of Bristol researcher Eugenio Proto writes.

3 Resilience: Laughter Is the Key to Resilience

Things happen at work – deadlines are missed, targets are

not met, there are misunderstandings and you can't always change that, but you can change the way you respond to them.

By laughing at what happens you will keep a clear mind, and come up with the solution much faster.

According to the Connor Davidson Resilience Scale, these are the most important attributes and laughter yoga exercises have been found to help with all of them:

😄 Coping with stress.
😄 Being able to bounce back.
😄 Not becoming discouraged by failure.
😄 Not letting anything get in your way.
😄 BELIEVING that you can achieve your goals.
😄 Being able to adapt to change.

Tip: Laughing on purpose takes practice, so try repeating, "ho-ho-ho, ha-ha-ha, he-he-he" for a few minutes and soon it will change to real laughter.

4 Creativity/Innovation: Laughter Boosts Creativity/Innovation

"Laughter is America's most important export." (Walt Disney)

Laughter is like creativity-juice for your brain. Being able to laugh at work frees you from stress and anxiety, two things that will drain your creativity faster than you can say "bruhaha." Free from a fear of being criticised or judged, you'll be more likely to think of creative solutions that are innovative.

Over fifty years of research on creativity has shown that playfulness and humour have a positive impact on the quantity of ideas and the quality of creative thinking in groups, which can lead to an increase in the organisation's innovative output.

There are times when you just can't feel inspired for many different reasons. A dose of laughter will energise you and get those creative juices flowing. Research shows that laughter will help solve problems by making it easier to think and the lighter mood leaves lots of room for that eureka moment, YAY!! So, get ready for some awesome ideas through laughter.

Happy people are more creative because their mood makes them more responsive and allows them to have more and better ideas.

5 Motivation: Are You Doing a Job that Motivates You?

☺ Laughter helps learning and motivation due to the important role it plays in the reward circuitry of our brains.

☺ Laughter produces dopamine, known as the 'reward hormone', which is responsible for regulating mood, motivation, learning and attention. The influx of dopamine activates the reward circuit in the brain, making us feel good and positive, and also motivated to move forward.

Tip: When in a stressful or dead-end situation, try taking a few minutes off to share a laugh with co-workers or maybe watch a stand-up routine. You'll find renewed motivation and focus when you go back to work.

YAY!! Let's laugh and get motivated today 😁😁

6 Team Engagement And Performance: Improve Your Team's Performance by Adding Laughter Online While Working from Home

Now more than ever you need to keep your staff engaged and performing to their best. There are so many challenges involved with working at home, so make it fun and easy for them.

😁 Do regular Laughter exercises.
😁 Find positive things to add to the call.
😁 Have a gratitude jar.
😁 Play games online.
😁 Get them to bring something that means a lot to them. This helps you get to know them and it will help you bond.
😕😕 Please be careful when telling jokes as people may find them offensive – laughter exercises are a much better way to get things going.

Appendix 6

Laughter and the Golden Years

This is something I wrote when I was on a trip to Istanbul, Turkey, which was inspired by watching a lonely old lady sitting on the road selling socks she had knitted.

People have a much higher life expectancy now and this is taking its toll and we really need to make some changes to help with the positive psychology of our wonderful folk of this age group.

I would like to talk about three areas where laughter can help bring more happiness into the lives of older people; and ours, after all, we are all heading that way too, so let's nip any problems in the bud now and help emotionally, socially and physically.

Emotionally

The lady I saw in Istanbul proves a point: her years of cooking, cleaning and dedicated care to her family showed on her body, hands, face and, especially, in her eyes. She had given so much to make sure everyone in her family was taken care of and yet here she was all alone. I bought a pair of socks from her and smiled, gleaming because I was happy to be with my children after not seeing them for four months. She returned a lonely, empty smile and that got me thinking.

We dedicate our lives to bringing up our kids and then set them free to be the best they can be, to put our hard work to use and hopefully be successful. Ironically, they do just that and often become very busy and move on, leaving their parents alone. It may not be intentional, it just happens, and families crumble, especially in the west where many seniors move into care facilities and residential homes.

Bouts of depression at any age are not fun but when your mental and physical faculties are not as they once were, it is even worse. Laughter Yoga releases the joy cocktail of oxytocin, dopamine, serotonin and endorphins to the brain and this helps lighten the mood.

Older people still want to be involved in everything, but the generation gap makes it hard for them to understand what is going on. Learning to laugh at life, at themselves and at their misunderstandings will make it easier to accept their situation.

Socially

One big problem is how to deal with loneliness. This is something that can be experienced during many stages of life, and not limited to seniors, of course. Older people suffer social losses greatly with age. Their social life is narrowed down by loss of work associates following retirement, death of relatives, friends or spouse, and weak health, which restricts their participation in social activities.

Home becomes the centre of their universe and that brings on a feeling of isolation.

There is good news; laughter really connects people and is a good source of human touch, community, a feeling of inclusion and a chance to step away from that dreaded feeling of being alone. Laughter Yoga Clubs are an amazing way to meet regularly and share a connection, which brings emotional comfort and solace.

Also, the more interaction people have, the easier and more confident they will feel to meet other new people, and this will help them have a great social life.

Tip: Feel free to contact me to find out where your nearest laughter club is and enhance your social interaction.

Physically

Our elders are dealing with a variety of health conditions and laughter really is the best medicine. It's a very passive workout and will get you moving and oxygenating your cells, which will promote better health.

A good regular Laughter Yoga workout will:

- Help strengthen a weakened immune system, which can help fight off viruses, bacteria and diseases.
- Help you feel energised and also promote improved sleeping habits.
- Will promote better mental health and help to deal with those bouts of depression.

- Improve heart conditions (hypertension, high blood pressure) – it's as good as cutting salt.
- Help regulate your blood sugar levels in conditions like diabetes.

These are just a few of the many benefits of laughter, constantly being researched, and it is really exciting to see that we have such a fun way to improve our health and well-being.

Appendix 7

Laughter Prescription by Janni Goss (from her book 'Love, Laughter and Longevity')

Laughter Prescription

Optimal Daily Dosage: 20 minutes of laughter

- Share your smile!
- Avoid bad news. Look for good news.
- Play, laugh and have fun with the people in your life, especially children.
- Access more comedy – TV, movies, DVDs, radio, print media and the internet.
- Be an optimist – have hope in your life.
- Exercise your sense of humour!
- Use humour to de-stress. Laugh at yourself.
- Find a laughter club and do laughter yoga!
- Seek help if laughter is elusive.
- Give thanks for the benefits of laughter!

www.jannigoss.com

Appendix 8

Finding Your Balance through Difficult Times:

The L>A>U>G>H>T>E>R Method will help you deal with adversity, helping to manage your emotions by understanding how they play a part in making decisions.

You will be able to identify stress responses and learn how to deal with overwhelm and how to adjust during turbulent times.

Understanding how to rewire your brain with these quick effective tips will help you be self-motivated, productive and eager to do whatever you put your mind to.

Laughter improves morale, motivation and engagement at home and also in the workplace.

The courses are tailor-made to your specific needs and outcomes required. Below you can see some of the topics covered in the course that can be used together or on their own. Courses vary from ninety minutes, half day, one, two and three day courses. Available online and in person for individuals and corporate businesses too.

These highly interactive courses are designed to help in applying them into your life and workplace immediately.

L>A>U>G>H>T>E>R Method:

L – Love and Laughter

How to love yourself.

Adding laughter into your life.

Learn the health benefits of laughter.

How loving others helps you achieve.

Learning to love what you have.

Learning to be grateful.

A – Actualisation of self

Values and beliefs.

Find out:

>   what you are good at

>   what you are not so keen to do – outsource

>   what you need

>   what success looks like to you

>   how you'll know you've reached success

>   what's holding you back

How to deal with your emotions.

Find out about your reward circuit.

U – Unpack, Unify

Creating habits that serve you.

How emotions play a part in decisions.

How to rewire the brain.

Using tapping to clear blocks.

Unpack, understand, forgive and let go.

How to motivate yourself and others.

The new you, the person you want to be.

G – Gaining knowledge through Gratitude

Ho'oponopono.

Gratitude jar.

Being grateful for what you're good at.

Accepting good things people say.

Assess what worked and what didn't – thanks for the lesson.

H – Harnessing Happiness

What is happiness?

Enteric nervous system.

Second brain in the gut.

How emotions affect our moods.

How the brain plays a part in our happiness:

   let it rest

   feed it

   let it play

   work it

T – Tools

Mental bank.

Laughter videos.

Tapping.

Meditation.

Gibberish.

Fun games.

Who am I?

Mission statement.

Talent jar.

Gratitude jar.

E – Esteem

Utilising and developing talents and abilities.

Pursuing goals.

Work on your strengths.

You are who you are.

R – Resilience

Identifying stress responses.

Understanding different types of stress.

How to deal with feeling overwhelmed.

Different types of meditation that can work for you.

How perfecting your communication can help with stress.

Resilience and optimism.

Dealing with conflict.

How to create rapport with others.

Creating a confident state of self.

About the Author

Jo-Dee Walmsley, who lives in Woking, England, has been described as 'effervescent, passionate and driven, with a sweetness that shines through her smile'.

When she's not doing keynotes and holding L.A.U.G.H.T.E.R Method Workshops abroad and online, she can often be found taking a cycle on the banks of the lovely Basingstoke Canal. She also loves to be cuddled up with her cat, Tigger, while they try to figure out how the criminal mind works, through watching true crime programmes.

She is very proud of being a thriving PKD warrior, who is on dialysis and waiting for a kidney transplant but still able to laugh at whatever life throws at her. She believes our circumstances don't have to define us, nor our happiness; we can choose to adapt our thought patterns and live the life we truly desire, no matter what.

Jo-Dee's mission is to spread joy and help people deal with turbulent times, which is why she is 'Licensed to Laugh' and heading your way soon.

Contact

Email: jodee@simplylaughter.com

Website: www.simplylaughter.com
and www.jodeewalmsley.com

Facebook group:
https://www.facebook.com/groups/laughterisyourlifeline

A message to my younger self...

If I could go back in time and speak to my younger self, I would want to tell her to trust her instincts. To know that you have got this, and you are more than enough. You don't need others to make you somebody; you are perfect the way you are. You are never given more than you can handle and it is OK to ask for help; you do not need to do this all alone. Always be true to your values and beliefs. Sometimes making an early sacrifice will help you avoid long-term suffering. Don't focus so much on your weaknesses, and let your strengths guide you. Be as kind to yourself as you are to others.

I wish I had known that I didn't have to wear myself down by fighting for every little thing. When things got in the way, it was probably a sign that it was not meant to be. Sometimes it is better just to let go and trust the process. Somehow the Universe knows what and who is good for us, and even though it doesn't always seem like what we think we need – it is. Don't take life so seriously; learning to love yourself and laugh at yourself early on would be helpful to deal with any situation.

Being able to survive everything I have been through has shown me that it is OK to fail, and that my experiences were all valuable lessons. We find ourselves in the same position time and time again if we don't learn the lesson.

Don't let fear get in the way of doing what you really want to do. Always trying to please everyone actually ends up hurting the people in your life and, most of all, yourself. Don't be afraid to speak up and let people know what you really think; their reaction may surprise you.

I now feel like all those lessons have made me the incredible, resilient, and loving person I have become. I am now able to confidently express how I am feeling and to go for what I want. I don't need to settle, because I deserve so much more. I know I can't change many things that happen, but I certainly can change the way I respond to them. I can also make sure I take responsibility for my life, and then I am in control of it. YAY!!

I am who I am, and I am more than OK with that. Hello world, here I come!

I am *The Girl Who Refused to Quit*.

Acknowledgements

To my dearest friend Angela Kelly, I certainly couldn't have done this without you. Thank you for your dedication in helping me get my message out the way I wanted it. We sure did have a laugh reading through my acrobatic grammar, and moments of brain fog, didn't we? You have been an amazing friend to me for over twenty years and I am so grateful to have you in my life.

Thank you, Dr Lynda Shaw, for writing my foreword. I have always been a huge fan of your work and loved learning from you when I did your Neuroscience Professional Development Programme. You helped me learn about the brain and how I could combine that with what I do. I am forever grateful.

To Grumpy Graham, thank you for being you, I truly value our friendship. You have stood by me through all my medical ups and downs, never leaving my side, thank you for taking such good care of me.

To Debbie Mather-Pike, you are not only my sister, but my best friend and I thank you for being my rock through 'sick' and sin.

Rebecca Anstey, my dear friend, we have been through a real roller coaster ride together over the past nineteen years and you have been there for me, encouraging me all the way. Thank you.

Thank you to The Lighthouse in Woking for picking me up and supporting me to build myself up again. To all the ladies in Nurture, you have been a great support, thank you.

A big thank you to my long-time friend Rhian Apgruffydd for taking time out of your busy schedule to help me with my amazing photographs. You have always supported me, and I truly appreciate that.

To all my NHS Renal Team, consultants, surgeons, doctors and nurses for dialysis and transplant, you have all been amazing looking after me. I am alive because of you. Thank you!

Thank you to all my family and friends all over the world, each one of you have played an important part in me becoming me.

Wow, Cassandra Farren from Heart-led Authors Academy, thank you. Somehow your book *Share Your World* made the difference. I have been wanting to write a book for over fifteen years lol and, suddenly, your book was all it took for me to do it. Thank you for your support and all those in your Heart-led Authors Academy Group that have really helped me along my journey.

Thank you to Jen Parker from Fuzzy Flamingo for designing my beautiful book cover. Thank you for all the amazing work you did on doing the editing, proofreading, typesetting and making the self-publishing process effortless. You have been a huge support and so awesome to work with.

Be a Lifeline and Save a Life

If you are in the UK and would like to apply to be a kidney donor for Jo-Dee please contact Tracy from the Renal team: tracy.norton2@nhs.net and mention it's for Jo-Dee Walmsley.

You can also make an altruistic donation to someone you don't know.

Be an organ donor: UK https://www.organdonation.nhs.uk/

For more information on Polycystic Kidney Disease (PKD): https://pkdcharity.org.uk/

Thank you

Printed in Great Britain
by Amazon